73062

FUNDAMENTALS OF
KERATINIZATION

A SYMPOSIUM PRESENTED AT THE NEW YORK MEETING
OF THE AMERICAN ASSOCIATION FOR THE ADVANCEMENT
OF SCIENCE, DECEMBER 30, 1960

Edited by

EARL O. BUTCHER
College of Dentistry, New York University

and

REIDAR F. SOGNNAES
School of Dentistry,
University of California at Los Angeles

Publication No. 70 of the
AMERICAN ASSOCIATION FOR THE ADVANCEMENT OF SCIENCE
Washington, D. C., 1962

Preface

Fundamentals of Keratinization is based on a two-session symposium held at the annual meeting of the American Association for the Advancement of Science in New York City, December 30, 1960.

Cosponsored by the AAAS Section on Medical Sciences (N), the American College of Dentists, American Dental Association, and the International Association for Dental Research, North American Division, the symposium was organized and prepared for publication by the Program Chairman and Secretary of the Section on Dentistry (Nd).

In keeping with the general philosophy of the Association, it has been the objective of the Section on Dentistry to bring many scientific fields to bear upon the elucidation of various biological mechanisms that are considered basic to oral health and contributory to the advancement of science (*Calcification in Biological Systems,* AAAS Publication No. 64, 1960; "Oral Aspects of Aging" in *Aging,* AAAS Publication No. 65, 1960).

In the symposium on Keratinization, a multidisciplinary group of eighteen authors and coauthors, representing such fields as dentistry, medicine, dermatology, anatomy, zoology and pathology, presented eleven reports, based on various newer techniques in histology, histochemistry, electron microscopy, tissue culture, chemistry, and physics, with a view to examine current information on those processes of growth and differentiation through which epithelial cells are transformed into biologically important keratinizing structures, such as certain parts of mucous membranes, skin, hair, nails, horns, claws, hoofs, pathological tissues and, most unique of all epithelial products, the "skin" of the teeth, the dental enamel.

Several of the reports dealt with the elaboration, structure, and chemistry of the cytoplasmic fibrils, keratohyaline granules, and other elements involved in keratin formation; one paper was concerned with various environmental and physical factors that influence keratinized tissue, including the effects of ultraviolet radiation, loss of water, and the shedding mechanism of the corneum of the skin; and two authors described the control and alteration of keratinization as influenced by vitamin A at various levels, when applied locally and administered systemically for therapeutic purposes.

Two studies on keratinization within the mouth, on the lining of pathological oral cysts and on the relation between keratinization and oral inflammation, were of particular interest to the dentist; and the concluding papers on the ultrastructure and chemistry of dental enamel provided intriguing new information on a calcifying organic matrix which—albeit of epithelial origin and subject to connective tissue influence—failed to reveal the typical fingerprints of either keratin or collagen.

A more detailed, but nevertheless fairly brief, consideration of the issues that still are somewhat controversial makes a few summarizing remarks seem in order.

Keratins in the past generally have been considered to be best classified as being either of a hard or soft variety. In "soft" keratin, epithelial cells pass through a granular and glossy stage while changing into such hornyfying structures as corneum, corns, and callouses, all of which contain relatively small or moderate quantities of sulfur. In the so-called "hard" keratin variety, on the other hand, the change into a horny substance is thought to occur in a more progressive fashion without any dominant granular and glossy layers, but with a relatively higher sulfur content. There still are contradictory views regarding this general classification, according to the authors of this monograph.

On the basis of *histological* examination, the division into soft and hard keratins may still serve a useful purpose. However, *histochemical* studies applied to a comparison between keratins from many sources suggest that the division of keratins into hard and soft varieties is an oversimplification. For instance, the epidermis, generally referred to as "soft," sometimes shows a distinct sulfydryl-rich keratogenous zone which is supposed to occur only in hard keratins. One point of distinction between the formation of hard and soft keratin is held to be the absence of keratohyaline granules in the production of the hard variety. But it has been argued, on the other hand, that the keratohyaline granules probably play no direct role in the formation of SH and SS groups because neither of these radicals is demonstrable by histochemical methods.

At the *ultrastructural* level, observations have been made on the cytoplasmic fibrils, granules, and other cellular constituents during transformation into keratin. In some keratins, fibrilar type of cytoplasmic elements appear to be mainly involved; in others both fibrils and granules appear to be bound together; and in a third type, no fibrils appear to participate. It has been suggested that keratohyaline transforms into fibrils of a 100-angstrom diameter and that tonofilaments and keratohyaline associate just prior to keratinization. Thus, one of the most likely functions of the keratohyaline granules may be to provide for stabilization of tonofilaments. Furthermore, it is striking that the electron microscopic observations of free RNP particles are closely associated with the keratinization process, especially during the early stage of keratohyaline granule formation.

Utilization of *tissue cultures* indicates that the basal cells of embryonic ectodermal derivatives are self-differentiating *in vitro*. In addition, cultures of pure ectodermal epithelium from adult skin have been shown to behave similarly to whole skin cultures. Therefore, connective tissue does not seem to be essential for the process of hyperkeratinization, which is known to accompany certain pathological states, including precancerous lesions.

Observation on the *physical* environment that affects epidermal keratin indicates that the skin normally loses water to the external milieu faster than it receives water from the underlying tissues. But this tendency for the skin to get dry is shown to be counteracted by the presence of certain hydrophilic substances which keep the stratum corneum from complete dehydration. Some of these hydrophilic substances, it is noted, are water soluble and hence removed by contact with water or detergent solutions. Thus the keratin of the body surface may be hydrated or dehydrated by environmental conditions, and result in intermittent swelling, breaking, roughening, and various degrees of shedding.

With respect to *metabolic* environment, two investigations are concerned with the control of keratinization by vitamin A. In contrast to the vitamin A deficiency state, in which various ectodermally derived structures, glands, and mucous membranes undergo keratinization, the application of large amounts of vitamin A locally to keratinizing mucosa (vagina) can dramatically modify the superficial layer of the epithelium, with the result that nucleated cells instead of the keratinized ones are produced. Though there is a significant increase in mitotic index of epidermis under the influence of vitamin A, this activity may be reduced with very high levels. Small amounts of vitamin A appear to stimulate cell division in normally keratinizing epidermis both *in vivo* and *in vitro*. At the biochemical level the mechanism of vitamin A action on epithelia may possibly involve some alteration of copper-catalyzed enzymes, presumably located in mitochondria.

Present knowledge may justify more rational use of vitamin A therapy in the treatment of leucoplakia; but the dose level, vehicle, and mode of application would seem to be more important than formerly suspected. For example, at lower dose levels hypertrophy appears to be predominant as a result of increased mitotic rate. At moderate dose levels parakeratosis is the major response. At higher dose levels mucous metaplasia ensues, and this is accompanied by changes in growth pattern of the epithelium, producing downgrowths, cysts, and glandlike structures. At still higher dose levels, death of the epithelium tends to occur. When the effect of vitamin A supplement has been determined in A-deficient rats, moderate dosage administered locally stimulates the A-deficient tissues, whereas high toxic doses have an inhibitory effect.

Keratinization of the *oral mucosa* varies a great deal both in degree and location. Parakeratosis has been found in approximately 60 to 70 per cent of human gingival biopsy specimens, whereas the remainder of the gum samples under study were fully keratinized or nonkeratinized. The alveolar mucosa is normally unkeratinized and invariably contains epithelial glycogen, whereas full keratinization is rare in the presence of either glycogen or inflammation. Parakeratosis, however, can occur in conjunction with the presence of glycogen or inflammation. Different degrees of physical stretch, rather than degrees of metabolic stress, may affect the variations in keratinization in different parts of the mouth, some areas being tightly fixed to dense connective tissue and bone, while others are subject to great flexibility.

Microscopic examination of *odontogenic cysts* has shown that a high percentage contained keratinized epithelium. The incidence of keratinization was highest among residual cysts (17%), the lower in the radicular cysts (10%); while the lowest percentage (7.1%) existed in follicular cysts. Curiously, twice as many keratinizing cysts were found in the mandible as in the maxilla. Simultaneously with keratinization, a PAS positive, diastase-resistant material was found. In general, it appeared that keratinization occurred when inflammation subsided and that this process developed in cysts of long standing, such as the residual cysts.

Justification for including the chapters on *dental enamel* arises from the fact that, evolutionary and embryologically, the protein of enamel is of ectodermal and epithelial origin and, generally, has been referred to as keratin. Newer electron microscopy observations have shown that a cell membrane always lies between the ameloblastic cytoplasm and the enamel matrix proper, indicating that the protein framework of the enamel is an extracellular product, while keratin in other epithelial structures is intracellular in its origin. Furthermore, in the chapter on the chemical and physical properties of enamel it is pointed out that the organic enamel matrix appears to have some structural features of the beta-keratins, especially in terms of the x-ray diffraction pattern. On the other hand, the enamel protein has certain chemical fingerprints of collagens in that it contains hydroxylysine, possibly some hydroxyproline (though this is still controversial), and large amounts of proline. Meanwhile, one cannot classify this epithelial derivative as being a typical keratin.

Many other questions of interpretation will arise as the chapters are read, but it is hoped that the symposium will provide a framework of reference regarding current knowledge and, more importantly, a source of stimulation for future studies.

EARL O. BUTCHER
Program Chairman

REIDAR F. SOGNNAES
Secretary, Section on Dentistry

Contributors

RUSSELL J. BARRNETT, Department of Anatomy, School of Medicine, Yale University, New Haven, Connecticut

HOWARD A. BERN, Department of Zoology and Its Cancer Research Genetics Laboratory, University of California, Berkeley, California

IRVIN H. BLANK, Department of Dermatology, Massachusetts General Hospital, Harvard Medical School, Boston, Massachusetts

J. HENRIKSEN, Department of Oral Pathology, The Royal Dental College, Copenhagen, Denmark

DONALD J. LAWRENCE, Department of Zoology and Its Cancer Research Genetics Laboratory, University of California, Berkeley, California

A. GEDEON MATOLTSY, Department of Dermatology, Boston University School of Medicine, Boston, Massachusetts

HERMAN MEDAK, Division of Oral Pathology, College of Dentistry, University of Illinois, Chicago, Illinois

JULIA MEYER, Division of Oral Pathology, College of Dentistry, University of Illinois, Chicago, Illinois

JEROME P. PARNELL, Department of Anatomy, State University of New York, Downstate Medical Center, Brooklyn, New York

H. P. PHILIPSEN, Department of Oral Pathology, The Royal Dental College, Copenhagen, Denmark

KARL A. PIEZ, National Institute of Dental Research, Bethesda, Maryland

JENS J. PINDBORG, Department of Oral Pathology, The Royal Dental College, Copenhagen, Denmark

EDWARD J. REITH, Department of Anatomy, New York University School of Medicine, New York City, New York

JOHANNES A. G. RHODIN, Department of Anatomy, New York University School of Medicine, New York City, New York

BURTON S. SHERMAN, Department of Anatomy, State University of New York, Downstate Medical Center, Brooklyn, New York

REIDAR F. SOGNNAES, Division of Oral Biology, School of Dentistry, University of California, Los Angeles, California

GEORGE SZABÓ, Department of Dermatology, Massachusetts General Hospital, Harvard Medical School, Boston, Massachusetts

MICHAEL L. WATSON, Departments of Pathology and Radiation Biology, School of Medicine and Dentistry, University of Rochester, Rochester, New York

Contents

1   Mechanism of Keratinization, by A. GEDEON MATOLTSY   1

2   Histochemical Distribution of Protein-Bound Sulfhydryl and Disulfide Groups in Vertebrate Keratins, by RUSSELL J. BARRNETT and REIDAR F. SOGNNAES   27

3   Cultivation of Skin, Pure Epidermal Sheets, and Tooth Germs *in vitro:* With a Note on the Effect of Vitamin A, by GEORGE SZABÓ   45

4   Ultrastructure of Keratin in Oral Mucosa, Skin, Esophagus, Claw, and Hair, by JOHANNES A. G. RHODIN and EDWARD J. REITH   61

5   Influence of Vitamin A on Keratinization, by HOWARD A. BERN and DONALD J. LAWRENCE   95

6   Effect of Vitamin A on Keratinization in the A-Deficient Rat, by JEROME P. PARNELL and BURTON S. SHERMAN   113

7   Effect of Environmental Factors on the Physical Characteristics of the Stratum Corneum, by IRVIN H. BLANK   133

8   Keratinization of the Oral Mucosa, by JULIA MEYER and HERMAN MEDAK   139

9   Studies on Odontogenic Cyst Epithelium: Keratinization in Odontogenic Cysts, by J. J. PINDBORG, H. P. PHILIPSEN, and J. HENRIKSEN   151

10   Extracellular Position of Enamel, by MICHAEL L. WATSON   161

11   Chemistry of the Protein Matrix of Enamel, by KARL A. PIEZ   173

Index   185

1

Mechanism of Keratinization*

A. Gedeon Matoltsy †
Department of Dermatology,
University of Miami School of Medicine, Miami, Florida

Various views were formulated in the past on the morphological and chemical aspects of keratinization. Most of these are specific in nature and refer to keratinization of a particular tissue or cell line and usually are not applicable without some complication to another tissue. More than ten years ago a general view presented by Leblond (1951) and Giroud and Leblond (1951) received considerable acceptance, and reference is still often made to it. During the past years many new data became available on the fine structure of the constituents of keratin-forming cells. Some of these support Giroud and Leblond's view, while others are contradictory. In the following, Giroud and Leblond's views on keratinization are recalled and the main points, requiring modifications, are discussed. Subsequently, newer views and findings are presented on keratinization.

Older Views on Keratinization

Giroud and Leblond (1951) distinguished soft and hard keratins and defined two forms of keratinization on the basis of morphologi-

* This work was supported by grants from the National Institutes of Health, PHS C-4036, 2G224, A-5779, A-5924, and by U.S. Army Contact No. DA-49-007-MD-731.
† Present address: Department of Dermatology, Boston University School of Medicine, Boston 18, Massachusetts.

cal appearance and chemical constitution, such as soft keratinization and hard keratinization. With regard to *morphological* manifestations, it was pointed out that in soft keratinization the epithelial cells pass through a granular and glassy stage while changing into horny cells. The epidermis, medullary cell line of the hair, inner root sheath of the hair follicle, corns, calluses, horse burr, eponychium of the nail, etc., were presented as examples of soft keratinization. In hard keratinization, the epithelial cells change progressively into horny cells without formation of granular and glassy layers. This may be observed in the cuticular and cortical cell lines of the hair, nail, horn, hoof, claw, etc. The role of alpha-keratin containing tonofibrils was greatly emphasized and little attention was paid to other cytoplasmic constituents. Giroud and Leblond saw basic similarities in both forms of keratinization by assuming "the universal presence of tonofibrils in structures undergoing keratinization." They found that tonofibrils are present not only in Malpighian cells but also in all other keratinizing cells, including the cornified cells. From the *chemical* viewpoint, soft keratinization was characterized by the presence of small or moderate quantities of sulfur; hard keratinization by accumulation of sulfur in large quantities. Sulfur was assumed to be present as cysteine, bound to polypeptide chains of the tonofibrils of the noncornified cells. When the epithelial cells reach maturity, the sulfhydryl groups of cysteine become oxidized. A resistant keratin is formed by the tonofibrils which are stabilized by disulfide bonds extending between adjacent polypeptide chains.

During the past years, valuable observations were made on the fine structure of keratin-forming cells by electron microscopic investigations. With regard to the mechanism of keratinization, Birbeck and Mercer (1957a,b,c) made the most significant contributions. These investigators demonstrated that keratin is a complex substance and that besides tonofibrils other cytoplasmic constituents also play an important role in formation of the horny substance residing in terminal cells of keratinizing tissues. In the cortical cell line of the hair, for instance, it was clearly demonstrated that the terminal horny product will be formed by both cytoplasmic filaments and an amorphous cement (Birbeck and Mercer, 1957a). With regard to Giroud and Leblond's views, it is also of specific interest that these investigators showed that keratin may be formed solely by accumulation of amorphous cytoplasmic granules. This may be observed best in the cuticular cell line of the hair (Birbeck and Mercer, 1957b). Keratin formed by amorphous cytoplasmic granules was also demonstrated in the medullary cell line of the hair and wool by Rogers (1959a).

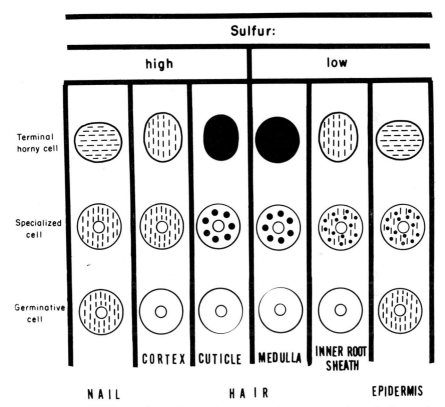

Fig. 1. The morphological manifestations of keratinization of the nail, mammalian epidermis, and various cell lines of the hair follicle are schematically illustrated, and the sulfur content of the terminal horny products is indicated. The examples shown on the left reveal that a high sulfur-containing horny product (hard keratin) may be formed by two different mechanisms. The examples on the right demonstrate that a low sulfur-containing material (soft keratin) also may be produced by two different mechanisms. Dashes indicate tonofibrils, dots cytoplasmic granules, solid black amorphous horny material, solid white absence of prekeratin.

In view of the above, a major problem arises with regard to tono-fibrils, which apparently can no longer be considered as the common precursor of keratin. Furthermore, since the morphological manifestations of keratinization in the cuticular and medullary cells of the hair are different from the other cell lines of the hair follicle or other tissues, the acceptance of only two forms of keratinization becomes problematic. The problem is illustrated in Fig. 1, using some of the examples which were given by Giroud and Leblond for hard keratinization (columns 1,2,3) and soft keratinization (columns 4,5,6). When the formation of amorphous keratin of the cuticular cell line of the hair (column 3) is compared with the production of fibrous horny material of the cortical cell line of the hair or nail matrix (columns 1,2), it is apparent that two different mechanisms may lead to the production of high sulfur-containing horny materials (hard keratins). Furthermore, it is readily recognizable that two forms of keratinization are involved in formation of low sulfur-containing terminal products (soft keratins). This is evident when the production of amorphous keratin of the medullary cell line (column 4) is compared with the formation of fibrous horny material in the inner root sheath or mammalian epidermis (columns 5,6). Accordingly, the above does indicate that the terms "hard keratinization" and "soft keratinization" require redefinition.

Newer Views on Keratinization

Keratinization may be considered as a specific form of cell differentiation in which metabolically highly active epithelial cells pass through various cytomorphic and physiologic changes while they reach the terminal stage and become filled with a resistant and considerably insoluble horny material (Matoltsy, 1960). In initiation and maintenance of the process, the entire tissue is involved, exogenous factors, such as dermal effects, vitamins, and hormones, also seem to play an important role.

It is characteristic of all keratinizing epithelia that they are built up of three different cell types, including germinative, specialized, and terminal horny cells. With regard to the mechanism of keratinization, it is important to recognize that the germinative cells of some

epithelia, such as epidermis, nails, claw, hoof, horn, beak, or keratinized tooth, characteristically give rise only to a single type of specialized cell and these in turn form a simple structure, consisting
of a single type of horny cells (Fig. 2, column 1). The germinative
cells residing in the root of the hair, wool, quill, feather, however,
are capable of giving rise to various specialized cell types which in
turn form a complex structure consisting of structurally and chemically different horny cells (Fig. 2, column 2). Differences occur between germinative cells not only in this regard but also in the production of prekeratin. The germinative cells of simple tissues are

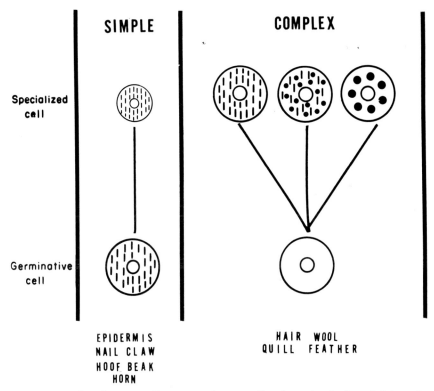

Fig. 2.   The drawings illustrate schematically that simple keratinizing tissues give rise only to a single type of specialized cell, while the complex tissues develop various specialized cell types. (The specialized cells of most
simple tissues contain tonofibrils. Those of the mammalian epidermis contain
both cytoplasmic fibrils and granules.)

already engaged to a limited extent in formation of prekeratin—in the form of tonofibrils—whereas those of the complex tissues are inactive in this regard.

The most important feature of the keratinization process is the production of differentiation products and their utilization in formation of the terminal horny material. From the *morphological* viewpoint it is significant that certain epithelial cells produce exclusively amorphous cytoplasmic granules, others cytoplasmic fibrils, and still others both fibrils and granules. The specialized cells which form only cytoplasmic granules yield an amorphous keratin. The cuticular line of the hair or wool is the best known example which keratinizes in this fashion. A fibrous terminal substance is produced by epithelial cells being primarily engaged in the synthesis of cytoplasmic filaments. The cortical cell line of the hair, wool, and quill are the best known examples which keratinize in this manner. Most of the simple tissues (Fig. 2, column 1) may also be considered to follow this pattern. The specialized cells of the mammalian epidermis and the inner root sheath of the hair follicle are examples which form both cytoplasmic fibrils and granules. The terminal material in these cases is also fibrous in character. Accordingly, it seems that largely three forms of keratinization may be distinguished on a morphological basis; one which is elaborated through formation of amorphous cytoplasmic granules, another through production of cytoplasmic fibrils, and a third one through manufacture of both cytoplasmic fibrils and granules, such as the keratohyalin and trichohyalin granules. The different forms of keratinization are shown in Fig. 3, with their characteristic stages, illustrated schematically.

The electron microscopic studies of Birbeck and Mercer (1957a), Brody, (1959a,b) and Rogers (1959a), greatly contributed to the better understanding of the finer details of the mechanisms listed in Fig. 3. Formation of *amorphous* keratin has been studied in detail in the cuticular cell line of the hair. It is characteristic of this process that the presumptive cortical cells develop very small granules, about 300 Å in diameter, at scattered points of the cytoplasm. During maturation of the cell, the granules increase in size by coalescence. The large droplets fuse into an amorphous mass at the

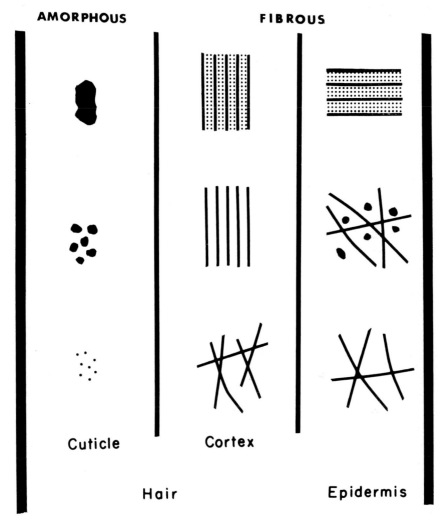

Fig. 3. Schematic presentation of stages in various forms of keratinization. Dots indicate cytoplasmic granules, lines cytoplasmic filaments. The small dots between parallel lines indicate an amorphous cementing material.

final stage. According to Birbeck and Mercer (1957b), about two-thirds of the terminal cuticular cell is filled with this amorphous material, the rest consists of nuclear and cytoplasmic remnants. Formation of *fibrous* horny material, through production of cytoplasmic fibrils and an amorphous cement, proceeds in the cortical cells of the hair in the following way (Rogers, 1959a). At the initial stage of the process, the main activity is synthesis of fine filaments, measuring about 60 A in diameter. At a later stage the filaments are more actively produced and also become aligned parallel with the long axis of the hair. When the cells reach the keratogenous zone, an amorphous cement, assumed to be rich in sulfur, accumulates and is deposited between the filaments. Subsequently, fibrillar units are formed consisting of bundles of filaments cemented together by the amorphous substance. Birbeck and Mercer (1957a) estimate a ratio of 1:1 for filaments and cement. Formation of *fibrous* horny material through production of cytoplasmic filaments and granules was investigated in detail in both the mammalian epidermis and in the inner root sheath of the hair follicle. In the epidermis of the guinea pig skin, stained with uranyl nitrate, Brody (1959b) noted fine filaments and small particles, 100 to 250 A in diameter, dispersed in the Malpighian cells. He found that during maturation of the cells the fine particles aggregate and form keratohyalin granules. He also noted that the terminal horny material consists of filaments between which an amorphous cementing material is deposited. Since the staining properties of the cementing material were identical to the fine particles constituting the keratohyalin granules, Brody (1959a) assumes that the interfibrillary material of the terminal product is derived from keratohyalin granules. The ratio of filament to cement was calculated 2:3. Birbeck and Mercer (1957c) and Mercer (1958) formulated a different view with regard to the fate of keratohyalin granules. These investigators assume that the substance forming the keratohyalin or the trichohyalin granules undergoes fibrous transformation. They also postulate that fibrous keratohyalin, or trichohyalin, together with the tonofilaments forms the terminal product.

From the *chemical* viewpoint, keratinization appears as a complex process, its details are very poorly understood. A major activity is the synthesis of fibrous or amorphous proteins which will be retained by the cell. Utilization or elimination of non-keratin constituents also appears as an important activity. Formation of *amorphous* horny material appears as a relatively simple process, including synthesis of end proteins and their aggregation into an amorphous mass. The amorphous material accumulating in the cells of the cuticular cell line of the hair is known as a highly resistant and heterogeneous substance containing sulfur in large quantities (Geiger, 1944a,b). Considerable evidence exists that it consists of two main fractions, a trypsin-resistant and a trypsin-digestible one (Mercer and Rees, 1946a,b; Lindberg *et al.*, 1949; Fraser and Rogers, 1955; Ramanathan *et al.*, 1956). The amorphous material formed in the medullary cell line is poorly stabilized and contains sulfur only in traces (Barrit and King, 1931; Bekker and King, 1931; Blackburn, 1948; Lloyd and Marriott, 1933; Matoltsy and Balsamo, 1955). The formation of the *fibrous* horny substance is more complex than that of the amorphous material. It includes the synthesis of a fibrous end protein and the production of an amorphous interfibrillary cement and association of these two into a highly organized system. Synthesis of the fibrous protein (α-keratin) is most probably identical in both forms of keratinization (Fig. 3, columns 2,3), whereas significant differences seem to prevail in the production of the amorphous cement. Association of sulfur-rich and sulfur-poor constituents in different ratios certainly is an essential factor that determines the stability and chemical properties of the terminal product. Exact data on the sulfur content of the components or on the site of the —S—S— bonds in these complex systems are not available. The proteins isolated from the wool and epidermis are of some significance to this problem. Alexander and Hudson (1954) and Rogers (1959b) obtained various fractions from the wool, some of which were fibrous, others amorphous in character. Rudall (1952) isolated a fibrous (epidermin) and a globular protein from the epidermis of the cow's nose. Matoltsy (Matoltsy, 1956, 1958; Matoltsy and Balsamo, 1955) extracted from the horny layer of the human skin a protein, soluble in neutral buffers (keratin A) and another one, soluble in highly alkaline solutions (keratin B). Each of the above preparations are of considerable interest for understanding the composition of the terminal horny product, but at the present time it is very difficult to judge the exact site of their origin and their relation to the constituents of horny cells.

In view of the above, it is quite clear that a horny structure, often defined in the past as "keratin" is of considerable complexity. A better understanding of horny substances and the chemical aspects of keratinization most probably will come only after identification and proper characterization of the constituents which form the terminal products of simple keratinizing tissues and cell lines of the complex tissues.

NEWER FINDINGS ON KERATINIZATION OF THE MAMMALIAN EPIDERMIS

Cytoplasmic fibrils and keratohyalin granules occur in abundant quantities in epidermal cells located next to the keratogenous zone. After transformation of granular cells into keratinized cells, the keratohyalin granules are no longer recognizable. Their mode of formation, function, or fate is not very well understood and very little that is definite is known about their chemical nature. Because of their stainability with basic dyes, such as hematoxylin, keratohyalin granules were first thought to be derivatives of the nucleus. This belief was abandoned only when it was shown that keratohyalin granules are Feulgen-negative and that the amount of nuclear material of granular cells is not less than, but identical to, the amount present in the nucleus of spinous or basal cell types (Leuchtenberger and Lund, 1951). Histochemical tests used for the purpose of determining the chemical nature of keratohyalin granules led to controversial results and views. While some investigators found that the granules are digestible with ribonuclease (Leuchtenberger and Lund, 1951; Smith and Parkhurst, 1949) or lipase (Jarrett, 1960), others reported negative results for ribonucleic acids (Lansing and Opdyke, 1950) or lipids (Spier and Caneghem, 1957). It was also found that keratohyalin granules contain dopa oxidase and mucopolysaccharides (Jarrett, 1960; Flesch and Esoda, 1960) and that PAS-positive carbohydrates are absent (Spier and Caneghem, 1957). The problem became further confused when it was shown by Barrnett and Seligman's technic that the granules contain no protein-bound sulfhydryl groups (Barrnett and Seligman, 1953; Eisen *et al.*, 1953), a chemical bond one would expect to find in a precursor of the horny component. Since then some investigators have proposed that keratohyalin represents a cytoplasmic debris, a side product of keratinization (Flesch, 1956; Selby, 1956), whereas others have maintained that it is the precursor of the horny component (Laden *et al.*, 1957).

The investigations described in the following were undertaken mainly for a better understanding of the role of keratohyalin granules in keratinization of the mammalian epidermis. Toward this end the granular cells and the keratinizing cells of the epidermis of human skin and the newborn rat skin were studied in the light microscope and the electron microscope. The reactivity of their constituents was also tested toward various chemical agents. The skin of newborn rats proved to be a most satisfactory tissue for our purposes for the following reasons. The epidermis contains an unusually thick stratum granulosum, consisting of a layer three to four cells thick, and the granular cells contain numerous and large keratohyalin granules (Fig. 4). Furthermore, it was noted that upon treatment with trypsin the epidermis separates in the form of a clean sheet without the components of the hair, and such sheets yield a very adequate starting material for isolation of keratohyalin granules.

Electron microscopic studies, in principle, revealed identical morphological manifestations in both experimental materials; variations were noted mainly in shape and size of keratohyalin granules.

Method

Skin samples were taken near the midline of the back of rats varying in age from 1 to 3 days. Skin samples from adult humans were removed from the thigh region. The samples were cut into small pieces and immediately immersed into ice-cold 1% osmium tetroxide buffered to pH 7.2, according to Palade (1952). The fixation time varied from 20 minutes to 1 hour. After dehydration in ethyl alcohol, the skin was embedded in a mixture of *n*-butyl methacrylate and methyl methacrylate. Sections were cut with a Porter-Blum microtome, floated on 10% acetone, and picked up on carbon-coated grids. The specimens were examined in an RCA EMU-3 electron microscope.

Investigation of the epidermis of the *newborn* rat showed that the granular cells contain numerous keratohyalin granules closely associated with a fibrous cytoplasmic network (Fig. 5). In the upper granular cells some of the nuclei appeared to have degenerated, and

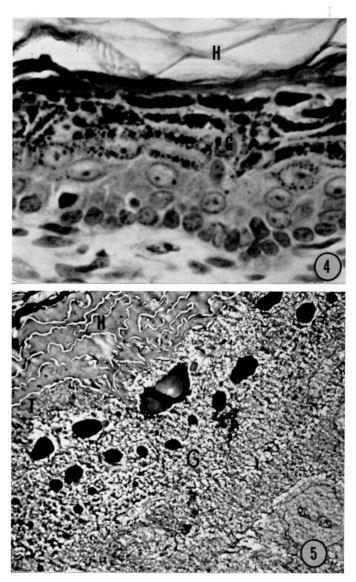

Fig. 4. Photomicrograph of a section of a two-day-old rat skin, stained with hematoxylin and Biebrich Scarlet. The stratum granulosum (G) consists of a 3- to 4-cell-thick layer and contains numerous darkly stained keratohyalin granules. The large dark bodies below the keratogenous zone appear as artifacts formed by clumping of the granules and by dye uptake in excess quantities. The stratum corneum appears split and reveals strongly flattened horny cells (H) (about ×640).

mitochondria occurred in small quantities. In the lower granular cells the nuclei were intact, mitochondria were abundant, and cytoplasmic particulates occurred in large amounts. Desmosomes appeared at points of attachments between granular cells and their neighboring cell.

The keratohyalin granules showed no preference with regard to location; they occurred in large quantities around the nuclei, near the cell membrane, and also were scattered through the cytoplasm. Their size varies greatly. Large granules, measuring 1.5 to 4.5 microns in length, were mostly seen in cells of the upper levels. Small granules, measuring 0.2 to 1.5 microns in diameter, were present in the cells of the lower levels. The large keratohyalin granules were often irregular in shape; the small ones appeared oval or round. The main body of most of the granules was homogeneous. In some granules, however, highly dense small particles were resolved in areas of lower density, indicating a fine granular substructure. None of the granules was separated from the cytoplasm by a limiting membrane; all of them were embedded and closely associated at the periphery with the filaments of the cytoplasmic network.

Serial sections showed that transformation of granular cells into horny cells proceeds individually, and no separate layer of transforming cells is present above the granular layer. At most places, strongly flattened keratinized cells were seen lined up in a dense and continuous layer above the granular cells. The most characteristic feature of the keratinized cells was that they contained no nuclei, and the keratohyalin granules were not recognizable. The width of the keratinized cells, six to ten times less than that of the underlying granular cells, indicated that they underwent intense flattening.

The transforming cells characteristically contained keratohyalin granules and some other cytoplasmic constituents in various stages of disintegration. Such cells were only occasionally seen at various parts of the epidermis (Figs. 6, 7, and 8). Nuclei were either en-

Fig. 5. Electron micrograph of a thin section of a two-day-old rat epidermis showing granular (G) and horny cells (H). On the left a granular cell in transformation (T) can be seen. Keratohyalin granules occur in the granular cells (G) in various shapes and sizes. They are very dense and are associated with cytoplasmic fibrils (×1280).

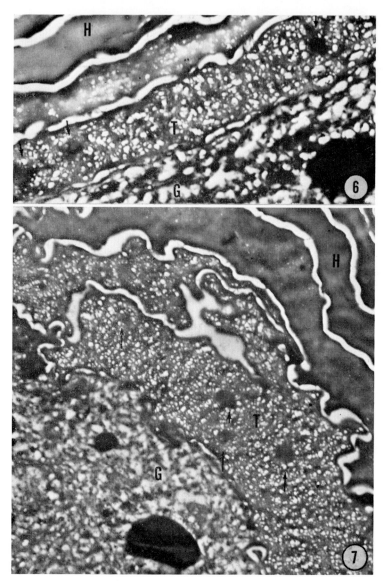

Fig. 6. Electron micrograph shows part of a granular cell (G), a granular cell in transformation (T), and horny cells (H) of a two-day-old rat skin. The granular cell in transformation (T) is in an advanced stage. The keratohyalin granules appear almost entirely fused with the fibrous content (arrow) (×12,750).

Fig. 7. Electron micrograph shows a granular cell (G), a granular cell in transformation in an early stage (T), and horny cells in a two-day-old rat skin. Note disintegrating keratohyalin granules in the transforming cell (arrow) and the numerous invaginations and extrusions of the cell body (×12,750).

14

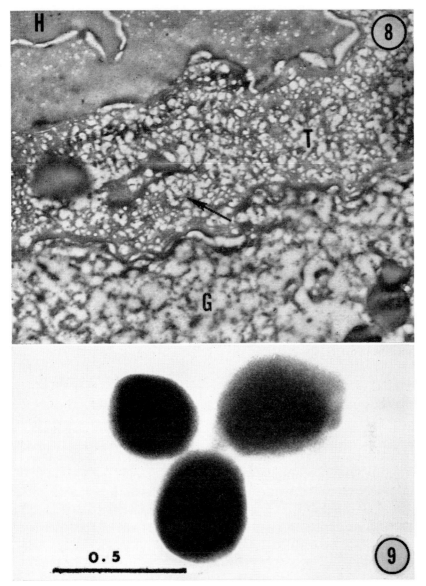

Fig. 8. Electron micrograph shows a granular cell (G), a transforming cell (T), and horny cells (H) in a two-day-old rat skin. Note disintegrating keratohyalin granules (arrow) in the transforming cell (T) (×17,000).

Fig. 9. Electron micrograph shows isolated keratohyalin granules, obtained from the skin of one-day-old rats. Note fine granular substructure in areas of low density (×75,000).

15

tirely absent or only the nuclear membrane and some remnant of the nuclear material was present. The main components of these cells were clumped tonofibrils and disintegrating keratohyalin granules (Fig. 8). The transforming cells, in the early stages, appeared collapsed, and their content was more concentrated than that of the granular cells (Fig. 7). The numerous invaginations and extrusions of the cell body in this early stage were indicative that dehydration was in progress. At advanced stages the cells flattened out, and their content was more condensed. The keratohyalin granules were usually difficult to recognize (Fig. 6).

The keratohyalin granules of the *human* epidermis were much smaller and quite irregular in shape (Fig. 10). They were dispersed in all parts of the cytoplasm and were tightly associated with cytoplasmic filaments. Occasionally they appeared more numerous around the nucleus than in other parts of the cell. Transforming granular cells revealed essentially the same stages seen in the epidermis of the newborn rat. Transformation seemed to start with dehydration, followed by collapse and flattening of the cell and condensation of its content. Keratohyalin granules and other non-fibrous constituents were seen disintegrating and the dispersed material mixing with the fibrous constituents (Fig. 11). The horny cells showed greatly varying structures. Some revealed a fused content, others were highly fibrous, and still others showed alternating fused and fibrous regions.

On the basis of the above observations it was concluded that the epidermal cells keratinize independently of one another and that the process runs its own course in each cell. Both cytoplasmic filaments and keratohyalin granules appear as differentiation products formed for the purpose of becoming a major part of the final horny product. Our observations indicate that the ultimate fate of keratohyalin granules is dissociation and mixing with constituents of epithelial cells during a late stage of maturation.

The transformation process may be considered as the most critical stage of keratinization. It seems to be induced by loss of fluids. Since aggregation of constituents in transforming cells starts at a level when normally hydrated cells also occur, it is most probable that during early stages of transformation fluids are not lost by a

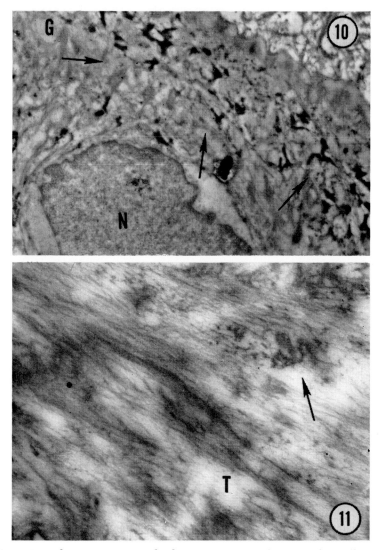

Fig. 10. Electron micrograph shows a portion of a granular cell (G) of the human epidermis. Dense keratohyalin granules (arrows) appear near the nucleus (N) and in the peripheral part of the cytoplasm (×10,800).

Fig. 11. Electron micrograph shows a portion of a transforming cell (T) of the human epidermis. Arrow points to disintegrating keratohyalin granules. Fine filaments represent fibrous epidermal keratin (×42,300).

simple desiccation and evaporation of water. Loss of fluids at this stage may be due to syneresis, denaturation, or some other process through which the proteins release their bound water (an active process). During advanced stages, when the cells are moved to a higher level desiccation and evaporation of free water molecules may be at work (a passive phase), leading to complete consolidation of the constituents.

In some other studies, observations were made on the chemical properties of the constituents of keratinizing cells by exposing skin fragments of the *newborn* rat to buffers, urea, and trypsin solutions. The changes caused by these agents were investigated under the light or in the electron microscope. Data were collected on the abundance of —SH groups and —S—S— bonds, by processing sections by the method of Barrnett and Seligman (1953).

Method

Three to five fragments of the back skin of newborn rats, each about 2 mm^2 in size, were immersed into 10 ml test fluid and stirred at room temperature for one hour. For histological studies the skin was fixed in 4% formalin, embedded in paraffin, and 8-micron sections were cut and stained with hematoxylin-Biebrich Scarlet. For electron microscopic studies the same procedures were used as described earlier in this paper. Sorensen's glycine-HCl and glycine-NaOH mixtures were freshly prepared for each experiment, and the final pH was determined with a Beckman pH meter. Urea solutions were made in 1 to 6M concentrations by dissolving urea in Earle's buffered salt solution. Trypsin was used in 0.1 and 1.0% concentrations dissolved in Ca and Mg free Earle's solution.

The significant data obtained in these studies are tabulated in Table I. They show that the horny component of cornified cells is only partially stabilized by —S—S— bonds and that free —SH groups also occur. This horny component, however, is a considerably resistant material, as it proved to be insoluble in buffers in the range from pH 1.5 to 10.9. It also resists the action of urea in 1 to 6M concentrations or trypsin in 0.1 or 1.0% solutions. It dissolved in solutions having a pH of 11.7 or 12.0, an alkalinity high enough to rupture the —S—S— bonds.

Although keratohyalin granules reveal properties similar to that of the horny component, such as resistance toward trypsin, they

Table. I.   Chemical Properties of Constituents of the New born
Rat Epidermis

	Horny Component	Keratohyalin Granules	Cytoplasmic Fibrils
Buffers			
Resisted	pH 1.5–10.9	pH 2.9–8.6	
Dissolved	pH 11.7	pH 10.1	
Urea			
Resisted	1–6M	1–3M	
Dissolved		4–6M	1–3M
Trypsin			
Resisted	0.1–1.0%	0.1–1.0%	
Dissolved			0.1–1.0%
—SH	+	—	
—S—S—	+	—	

also show significant differences, most probably due to absence of strong cohesive forces, such as the —S—S— bonds. Although they are stable in buffers in the range of pH 2.9 to 8.6 and resist urea in 1 to 3M concentrations, they pass into solution in urea of 4 to 6M concentrations, or in acid solutions of pH 1.9, or alkaline solutions in the range of pH 10.1 to 12.

The cytoplasmic fibrils of the granular cells appear poorly stabilized constituents. In the electron microscope they seem dissociated after treatment of the skin with 1 to 3M urea and entirely dispersed after using 0.1 to 1.0% trypsin.

With regard to the mechanism of keratinization, it appears significant that the keratohyalin granules consist of a considerably resistant substance and contain no —SH groups or —S—S— bonds. Since their dispersed material forms a part of the terminal product, it is reasonable to assume that it accounts in part for the relatively low sulfur content of the horny substance found in the cornified cells of the mammalian epidermis.

The results of the above studies were very helpful in establishment of a fractionation technic for keratohyalin granules, as they demonstrated that, with the exception of keratohyalin granules, all constituents of the noncornified cells may be dispersed or solubilized

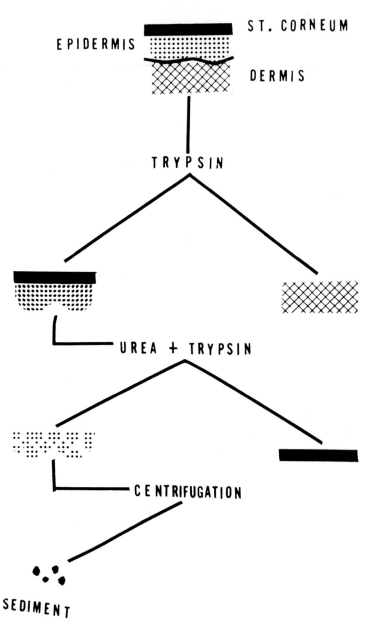

Fig. 12. Schematic illustration of the steps followed in fractionation of the newborn rat skin and isolation of keratohyalin granules.

in trypsin or in 1 to 3M solutions of urea. The various steps of the isolation technic are schematically illustrated in Fig. 12 and the details described as follows.

Method

The entire skin of 8 to 10 littermate newborn rats was removed and attached to a cardboard paper. Subsequently it was cut into small pieces of about 3–4 mm^2 in size. The skin fragments were then suspended in 10 ml of 1.0% trypsin and shaken for about 1 hour at 37°C. After this, the suspension was poured into a petri dish and inspected under a dissecting microscope. If separation was not complete and freely floating epidermal sheets were not present, shaking in trypsin was continued until satisfactory separation was obtained.

Clean epidermal sheets were selected under a dissecting microscope and transferred into Earle's solution for thorough washing. After this, the sheets were suspended in 5 ml of 2M urea and 1.0% trypsin dissolved in Earle's solution and were continuously shaken at 37°C. After 18 to 24 hours, the horny layer was floating on the surface, while the rest of the epidermis was dispersed in the solution. Fragments of the horny layer were removed with a glass needle and discarded. The suspension was allowed to stand for about 10 minutes, during which time the large undissolved tissue fragments spontaneously sedimented. Subsequently, the supernatant was decanted and centrifuged at 20,000g for 20 minutes. The sediment was then washed three times in distilled water by repeated resuspension and centrifugation.

The washed sediment was resuspended in 10 ml of 2M urea and 1.0% trypsin mixture and continuously shaken for 24 hours at 37°C. for further digestion and solubilization of the nonresistant components. It was then centrifuged at 20,000g for 10 minutes and washed three times in distilled water. The last sediment usually yielded a pure preparation of keratohyalin granules. If the preparation was contaminated with tissue fragments, the urea-trypsin treatment was repeated until a pure preparation was obtained. The quantity of keratohyalin granules isolated by the above technic was always small. Keratohyalin granules have not been collected in quantities large enough to permit chemical analysis.

Purity of the preparations was controlled by inspection in the phase contrast microscope and electron microscope. For electron microscopic studies the sediments were suspended in distilled water and serial dilutions were made. One drop of these was placed on carbon-coated grids and dried on filter paper in a petri dish.

Preparations of isolated keratohyalin granules studied in the electron microscope revealed larger and smaller aggregates of keratohyalin granules and indicated that they became tightly attached to each other during the isolation procedure. The electrons penetrated better through the less dense peripheral region of the granules than through the thick central portion. In such regions an extremely fine granular substructure was resolved (Fig. 9). No filaments were seen within the main body of the granules or attached to them.

Summary

1. Older views on keratinization are discussed in the light of newer findings and attention is called to the fact that besides tono-fibrils other cytoplasmic constituents may also play a primary role in the formation of "keratin."

2. Three forms of keratinization are distinguished on the basis of newer results. One is elaborated through the formation of amorphous cytoplasmic granules, another through production of cytoplasmic fibrils, and a third one through manufacture of both fibrils and granules.

3. Newer observations indicate that the epithelial cells of the mammalian epidermis keratinize individually, the process runs its own course in each cell. The main constituents of the horny component of cornified cells are derived from cytoplasmic fibrils and keratohyalin granules. Keratohyalin granules disintegrate at an advanced stage of cell maturation, and their material mixes with the fibrous cell constituents. Keratohyalin granules were found to contain no —SH groups of —S—S— bonds. They are, however, resistant to the action of trypsin, urea in 1 to $3M$ concentrations, and buffers in the pH range from 2.9 to 8.6.

4. An isolation technic is presented for keratohyalin granules.

Acknowledgment. The author wishes to thank Mrs. Margit N. Matoltsy for her valuable assistance during the course of the studies.

REFERENCES

Alexander, P., and Hudson, R. F. 1954. *Wool, Its Chemistry and Physics.* Reinhold Publishing Corporation, New York.
Barrit, J., and King, A. T. 1931. Note on the sulphur-free nature of medulla in blackface wool. *Biochem. J.,* 25: 1075–1076.

Barrnett, R. J., and Seligman, A. M. 1953. The histochemical distribution of protein-bound sulfhydryl groups. *J. Natl. Cancer Inst.*, 13: 905–925.

Bekker, J. G., and King, A. T. 1931. Sulphur distribution in the component structures of wool and porcupine quills. *Biochem. J.*, 25: 1077–1080.

Birbeck, M. S. C., and Mercer, E. H. 1957a. The electron microscopy of the human hair follicle. I. Introduction and the hair cortex. *J. Biopys. Biochem., Cytol.*, 3: 203–214.

Birbeck, M. S. C., and Mercer, E. H. 1957b. The electron microscopy of the human hair follicle. II. The hair cuticle. *J. Biophys. Biochem. Cytol.*, 3: 215–222.

Birbeck, M. S. C., and Mercer, E. H. 1957c. The electron microscopy of the human hair follicle. III. The inner root sheath and trichohyaline. *J. Biophys. Biochem. Cytol.*, 3: 223–230.

Blackburn, S. 1948. The composition and reactivity of medullated keratins. *Biochem. J.*, 43: 114–117.

Brody, I. 1959a. The keratinization of epidermal cells of normal guinea pig skin as revealed by electron microscopy. *J. Ultrastructure Research*, 2: 482–511.

Brody, I. 1959b. An ultrastructural study of the role of the keratohyalin granules in the keratinization process. *J. Ultrastructure Research*, 3: 84–104.

Eisen, A. Z., Montagna, W., and Chase, W. B. 1953. Sulfhydryl groups in the skin of the mouse and guinea pig. *J. Natl. Cancer Inst.*, 14: 341–354.

Flesch, P. 1956. Biochemical data on physiological and pathological epidermal keratinization. *J. Soc. Cosmetic Chemists*, 7: 521–530.

Flesch, P., and Esoda, E. J. 1960. Mucopolysaccharides in human epidermis, *J. Invest. Dermatol.*, 35: 43–46.

Fraser, R. D. B., and Rogers, G. E. 1955. The bilateral structure of wool cortex and its relation to crimp. *Australian J. Biol. Sci.*, 8: 288–299.

Geiger, W. B. 1944a. The scale substance of wool. *Textile Research J.*, 14: 82–85.

Geiger, W. B. 1944b. Scale substance of wool. *J. Research Natl. Bur. Standards*, 32: 127–130.

Giroud, A., and Leblond, C. P. 1951. Keratinization of epidermis and its derivatives, especially hair, as shown by x-ray diffraction and histochemical studies. *Ann. N.Y. Acad. Sci.*, 53: 613–626.

Jarrett, A. 1960. In *Progress in the Biological Sciences in Relation to Dermatology*, A. Rook, Editor. Cambridge University Press, Cambridge, England.

Laden, E. L., Gerthner, P., and Erickson, J. O. 1957. Electronmicroscopic study of keratohyalin in the formation of keratin. *J. Invest. Dermatol.*, 28: 325–327.

Lansing, A. I., and Opdyke, D. L. 1950. Histological and histochemical studies of the nipples of estrogen treated guinea pigs with special reference to keratohyalin granules. *Anat. Record, 107*: 379–397.

Leblond, C. P. 1951. Histological structure of hair, with brief comparison to other epidermal appendages and epidermis itself. *Ann. N.Y. Acad. Sci., 53*: 464–475.

Leuchtenberger, C., and Lund, H. Z. 1951. The chemical nature of the so-called keratohyalin granules of the stratum granulosum of the skin. *Exptl. Cell Research, 2*: 150–152.

Lindberg, J. E., Mercer, E. H., Phillip, B., and Gralen, N. 1949. The fine histology of keratin fibers. *Textile Research J. 19*: 673–677.

Lloyd, D. J., and Marriott, R. H. 1933. The distribution of sulphur in goat hair. *Biochem. J., 27*: 911–914.

Matoltsy, A. G. 1953. A study of the medullary cells of the hair. *Exptl. Cell Research, 3*: 98–109.

Matoltsy, A. G. 1956. Sedimentation studies of epidermal keratins: Keratin A and keratin B. *J. Biophys. Biochem. Cytol., 2*: 361–363.

Matoltsy, A. G. 1958. In *Biology of Hair Growth*, W. Montagna and R. A. Ellis, Editors. Academic Press, New York.

Matoltsy, A. G. 1960. Epidermal cells in culture. *Intern. Rev. Cytol., 10*: 315–351.

Matoltsy, A. G., and Balsamo, C. A. 1955. A study of the components of the cornified epithelium of human skin. *J. Biophys. Biochem. Cytol., 1*: 339–360.

Mercer, E. H. 1958. In *Biology of Hair Growth*, W. Montagna and R. A. Ellis, Editors. Academic Press, New York.

Mercer, E. H., and Rees, A. L. G. 1946a. Structure of the cuticle of wool. *Nature, 157*: 489–590.

Mercer, E. H., and Rees, A. L. G. 1946b. An electron microscope investigation of the cuticle of wool. *Australian J. Exptl. Biol. Med. Sci., 24*: 147–158.

Palade, G. E. 1952. A study of fixation for electron microscopy. *J. Exptl. Med., 95*: 285–299.

Ramanathan, N., Sikorski, J., and Woods, H. J. 1956. Electron microscope studies of the surface structure of wool and other fibers. *Biochim, et Biophys. Acta, 18*: 323–340.

Rogers, G. E. 1959a. Electron microscope studies of hair and wool. *Ann. N.Y. Acad. Sci., 83*: 378–399.

Rogers, G. E. 1959b. Newer findings on the enzymes and proteins of hair follicles. *Ann. N.Y. Acad. Sci., 83*: 408–428.

Rudall, K. M. 1952. The proteins of the mammalian epidermis. *Advances in Protein Chem., 7*: 253–290.

Selby, C. C. 1956. The fine structure of human epidermis as revealed by the electron microscope. *J. Soc. Cosmetic Chemists, 7*: 584–599.

Smith, C., and Parkhurst, H. T. 1949. Studies on the thymus of the mammal. II. A comparison of the staining properties of Hassall's corpuscles and of the thick skin of the guinea pig. *Anat. Record, 103*: 649–674.

Spier, H. W., and Caneghem, P. 1957. Zur Histochemie de Verhornung. *Arch. klin. exptl. Dermatol., 206*: 344–363.

2

Histochemical Distribution of Protein-Bound Sulfhydryl and Disulfide Groups in Vertebrate Keratins[*]

RUSSELL J. BARRNETT
Department of Anatomy, Yale University School of Medicine,
New Haven, Connecticut
        and
REIDAR F. SOGNNAES
Division of Oral Biology, School of Dentistry,
University of California, Los Angeles

Keratins are a group of tissue proteins of ectodermal origin found normally in the skin and its appendages. These proteins have certain chemical features in common. They are fibrous, resistant to digestion by pepsin or trypsin, and insoluble in water, dilute acids, or alkali, and various organic solvents. Keratins have been divided into two groups on the basis of the molecular ratios of the amino acids arginine, histidine, and lysine (Block and Vickery, 1931; Wilkerson, 1934). They have also been divided into two groups on the basis of solubility in strong acids (Unna and Golodetz, 1909) and by their x-ray diffraction patterns (Astbury, 1933; Astbury and

[*] These investigations were supported by grants from the National Institute of Arthritis and Metabolic Diseases (A-3688) and from the National Institute for Dental Research.

This work was initiated when the authors were members respectively of the Department of Anatomy, Harvard Medical School, and Department of Oral Pathology, Harvard School of Dental Medicine. The investigations were carried on with the technical assistance of George Pettengill.

27

Woods, 1930; Stoves, 1947). This in turn has given rise to the concept of two types of keratinization and two morphological types of keratin, "hard" and "soft" (Giroud et al., 1934; Giroud and Leblond, 1951).

Soft keratin is said to occur in the epidermis and internal root sheath and medulla of hair. Hard keratin is found in the cortex of hair and in nails, horns, hoofs, and claws. According to this concept the structures that contain soft keratin (as in epidermis) characteristically show a transitional area between the prekeratin zone (stratum Malpighii) and the keratinized zone (stratum corneum). The other characteristics are that it is supple and malleable, hence soft; it contains granular and glassy layers; it has a low or moderate content of sulfur; it is physiologically unstable; and it undergoes continuous spontaneous desquamation.

Hard keratin is tough and firm and the structures that contain it show a gradual transition from the prekeratin zone to the keratinized zone without the sharply delimited zones found in soft keratin. This area of gradual transition has been called the "keratogenous zone" and is said to occur in all keratinized appendages (Giroud and Leblond, 1951). The content of sulfur is high, and the structure does not desquamate. Furthermore, it is reported for hard and soft keratinization that the prekeratinous areas contain free sulfhydryls which disappear and are presumably oxidized to disulfides in the keratinous areas (Giroud and Bulliard, 1930; Percival and Steward, 1930; Chevremont and Frederic, 1943; Giroud and Leblond, 1951). In addition, the keratogenous zone of hard keratin is said to be characterized by an intensification of the sulfhydryl reaction just below the "keratinized zone" (Giroud and Leblond, 1951).

The intent of the present paper is to reexamine some of the above morphological concepts in the light of the distribution of sulfhydryl and disulfide groups in various vertebrate keratins with newer and specific histochemical methods. The use of these methods are, in essence, a handle to enable morphological examination of various keratins which have a high content of these sulfur-containing amino acids, and to state something of their relative amounts and distributions. This work has been collected over a period of eight years and while in progress has been reviewed briefly elsewhere (Barrnett, 1953, 1955; Barrnett and Sognnaes, 1955).

Materials and Methods

A large number of vertebrate keratins were collected. These included: from *fish*, skin and teeth of the lamprey eel; from *amphibia*, skin of frogs, toads, and salamanders; from *reptiles*, skin and scales of several species of poisonous and nonpoisonous snakes; from *birds*, feathers, beaks, claws, and spurs from six different species; from *mammals*, epidermis and hair of ten different species including man, pangolin scales, hoofs of rhinoceros and horse, horns of rhinoceros and bush buck, porcupine quills, and nails or claws of four species. These tissues were fixed in 80% alcohol containing 1% trichloroacetic acid. The softer tissues were embedded in paraffin and sectioned in the routine manner. The harder ones were embedded in N-butyl methacrylate. In these cases, thin sections (1 micron) could be cut easily by glass or steel knives, and these sections were freely permeable to the histochemical reagents.

Since the collection of the data on keratinous tissues has gone hand in hand with the development of seven different histochemical methods for revealing sulfhydryls and disulfides (Barrnett and Seligman, 1952, 1954; Seligman *et al.*, 1954; Barrnett *et al.*, 1955; Tsou *et al.*, 1955), all the methods were used at one time or another. However, all the tissues reported here were stained with the DDD (2,2′-dihydroxy-6,6′-dinaphthyl disulfide) method (Barrnett and Seligman, 1952) which is now considered the most specific available histochemical method for demonstrating sulhydryls and reduced disulfides.

Results

Since the cortex of hair has been frequently used as a model for hard keratins, it will be described first. The lower portion of the bulb showed a weak to moderate sulfhydryl reaction, but the upper part was moderately rich in these groups (Figs. 1 and 2). The papilla reacted weakly if at all (Fig. 2). Extending distally from the bulb, the histochemical reaction for sulfhydryls in the developing hair cortex occurred with progressive intensity until a region about one-third up the hair shaft, where the reaction was very in-

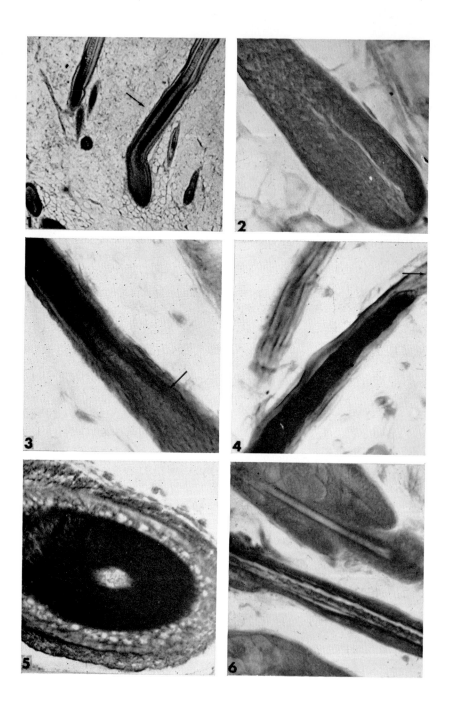

tense (Figs. 3 and 4). In fact, in no keratogenous tissue examined was the reaction more intense. The increasingly strong reaction in the hair cortex appeared first as peripherally placed intercellular and possibly intracellular fibrillary structures just above the bulb (Figs. 3 and 5). These fibrils became progressively more intensely stained and closely packed so that at the keratogenous zone (Giroud and Bulliard, 1930), the appearance was one of a nearly homogeneous and intensely stained matrix. Distal to this region, the cortex revealed no free sulfhydryls; the reaction ended in a moderately abrupt manner (Figs. 4 and 6).

The distribution of disulfides was quite different. The outer two-thirds of the hair shaft which was completely negative for sulfhydryls (Fig. 6) was very strongly reactive (Figs. 7–9). The reaction for these groups was less intense and was scattered in some of the substance of the keratogenous zone, where the sulfhydryl reaction was most intense, but was otherwise absent from the proximal parts of the hair shaft and bulb. The reaction was localized in the fibrillar substance of the hair cortex which appeared to arise from a sulfhydryl-containing precursor that was a product of the cells distal to the hair bulb.

Fig. 1. Section of albino rat skin showing the distal portion of hairs stained for sulfhydryls. The moderate reaction in the cells of the bulb is clearly discernible as well as the reaction of increasing intensity in developing hair cortex, especially in the keratogenous zone (arrow). The medulla and the root sheaths are weakly to moderately reactive (×90).

Fig. 2. Bulb of a hair showing a negative reaction of the papilla and the positive reaction of the epithelial cells (×360).

Fig. 3. Immediately above the bulb, the cells of the developing hair cortex are moderately positive for sulfhydryls and contain some obvious dense fibrils that react strongly (arrow). Just above this region (upper part of micrograph) is the beginning of the keratogenous zone, a region containing closely packed, intensely reactive fibrils (×360).

Fig. 4. Just above the previous micrograph is the further extension of the intense reaction of the keratogenous zone of the cortex, which has lost its fibrous appearance and is rather glassy in appearance. The reaction in the cortex of this hair ends rather abruptly (arrow) (×360).

Fig. 5. Cross section through the keratogenous zone showing the moderate reaction for sulfhydryls in the root sheaths and the intense reaction of the fibrils of the cortex (×360).

Fig. 6. Above the keratogenous zone the hair cortex is completely unreactive. The medulla and the root sheaths of the hair as well as the cells of a sebaceous gland are moderately positive (×360).

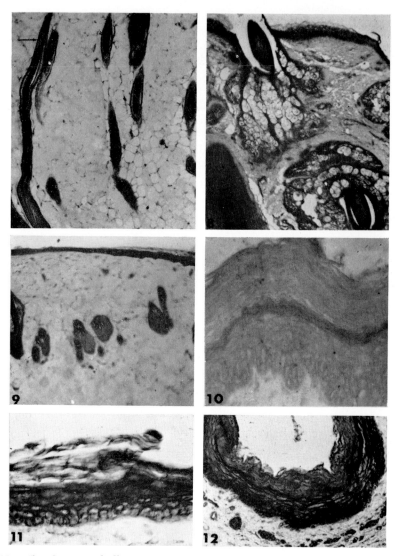

Fig. 7.   Section of albino rat skin stained for sulfhydryls and disulfides and indicating the hair cortex above the keratogenous zone (arrow) which was negative for sulfhydryl is now intensely reactive (×80).

Fig. 8.   Even the hairs in a dermoid cyst of the ovary taken from a human patient are reactive for sulfhydryl and disulfides (×240).

Fig. 9.   Photomicrograph of albino rat's skin showing cross section of the distal portion of the hair containing a cortex that is strongly reactive for disulfides. The stratum Malpighii of the epidermis is also intensely reactive (×80).

32

The distribution of these reactions is indicative of the fact that sulfhydryls are oxidized to disulfides in the region corresponding to the upper limits of the keratogenous zone of the hair shaft. Because of this finding which would suggest that the process of keratinization requires such oxidation (Giroud and Leblond, 1951), other hard keratins were studied.

A situation almost comparable with that found in animal hairs existed in lamprey teeth (Sognnaes and Lustig, 1955). In the lamprey an outer horny or functional tooth protrudes from the epidermis of the mouth and is periodically shed. Beneath this functional tooth is a vertical series of one or two developing replacement teeth with a germinating tooth bud at the bottom of the series. The teeth are separated by a stellate reticulum-like structure, except at the lateral margins where epidermal cells intervene. The similarity of histochemical reaction with animal hairs arises from the fact that the outer horny tooth is strongly positive for disulfides and contains only a few free sulfhydryls whereas the reverse is true of the tooth bud. The intervening replacement teeth showed a variable reaction depending on the stage of development. The first replacement tooth under the functional one showed a weak sulfhydryl reaction at its apex and at the base of the conical tooth but a strong reaction for disulfides throughout the tooth. The second replacement tooth, just above the bud, showed a strong reaction for both sulfhydryls and disulfides throughout (Figs. 13 and 14). In this respect, then, the tooth bud would be homologous with the hair bulb and the outer functional tooth with the outer portion of the hair cortex. The differences between the two structures were that precursor cells in the tooth bud contained more sulfhydryls than the hair bulb, and that a keratogenous zone where the content of sulfhydryls increased over that of the germinative layers was absent

Fig. 10. Section of epidermis of armadillo stained for sulfhydryls alone. Note that the entire structure is reactive and contains a zone of intensified staining that corresponds in region to the stratum granulosum ($\times 480$).

Fig. 11. Section of rat epidermis stained for both sulfhydryls and disulfides. Note the intense reaction that extends from the stratum basalis to the corneum ($\times 280$).

Fig. 12. Section of rat esophagus stained for sulfhydryls. Note that the peripheral parts of the cells of the stratum Malpighii are strongly reactive and there is an increased zone of staining in the stratum granulosum ($\times 200$).

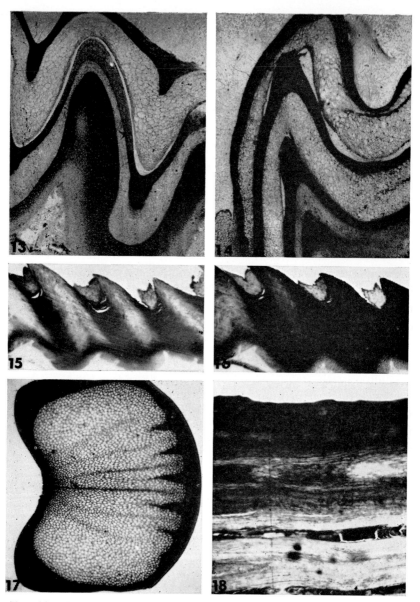

Fig. 13.   Section of lamprey tooth stained for sulfhydryls. The tooth germ is strongly reactive for sulfhydryls whereas the replacement tooth reacts mainly at the conical base. The outer functional tooth shows a weak and spotty reaction; most of that showing is primarily its natural color (×31.5).

Fig. 14.   Section of lamprey tooth stained for both sulfhydryl and disulfides. The outer functional tooth and the two replacement teeth show strong activity indicating a content of primarily disulfide groups. The inner tooth germ shows no increase in reaction over that of sulfhydryls (×31.5).

34

in the teeth, unless the bud is representative of that area also. In addition, the oxidation of sulfhydryls to disulfides was not as complete in the horny lamprey teeth as it was in hair and what oxidation had occurred was not as restricted in its localization in the teeth as it was in hair.

The latter two findings were borne out in all other instances of the investigations of hard keratins. For example, in the rodent claw, there are a fibrillar superficial stratum and a deep stratum that develop from the germinal matrix. A weak to moderate sulfhydryl reaction usually occurred in both strata, especially the superficial one. In the claws of birds, the deep stratum usually contained more free sulfhydryls. These strata in all animals were strongly reactive for disulfides. The cells of matrices of the claws were sulfhydryl-positive throughout, especially in the distal portion where the disulfide reaction was also especially intense (Figs. 23 and 24). This region could not be referred to as a keratogenous zone from a histochemical point of view because of the overlap of sulfhydryl- and disulfide-containing fibrils and the existence of sulfhydryl-positive fibrils distal to it. Histologically, however, it was a zone of gradual transition of fibrils to claw matrix. The spurs of birds were similar to claws in that the deep stratum of the fully formed structure usually contained more sulfhydryls than the superficial one. In human finger nails, there were fewer, but still some, sulfhydryl-positive fibrils in the fully formed portion of the nail distal to the matrix. These fibrils tended to occur in both the deep or superficial portion of the nails, leaving a midregion relatively free of sulfhydryls (Fig. 21). All portions were rich in disulfides (Fig. 22). The reactions of the matrix of the nail was quite similar to human epidermis of other

---

Fig. 15.   Section through the outer epidermal modification of duck's beak stained for sulfhydryls. The stratum Malpighii is moderately reactive whereas the stratum corneum shows a patchy reaction with areas of activity alternating with unreactive areas ($\times 31.5$).

Fig. 16.   With a reaction for both sulfhydryl and disulfides, there is an increase in staining in both the stratum Malpighii and the corneum ($\times 31.5$).

Fig. 17.   Cross section through the distal portion of a chicken feather stained for sulfhydryls alone. Contrary to what is found in the distal portion of hairs, the lateral walls and pith of the shaft are strongly reactive ($\times 31.5$).

Fig. 18.   Even rhinoceros horn contains free sulfhydryls in the fully keratinized portion ($\times 90$).

regions. The distal portion of the matrix (stratum corneum) was more reactive for both sulfhydryls and disulfides than the proximal (stratum Malpighii). However, a sharp demarcation of sulfhydryl from disulfide positive fibrils was also lacking in these structures.

Snake scales, formed by a folding of epidermis on the dermis, were positive for both sulfhydryls and disulfides. Although it is true that the outer horny projection of the scale contained more disulfides than sulfhydryls, the distribution of chemical groups was quite similar to that in the epidermis and will be covered later. It should be reiterated that in these structures, as in most of the others mentioned in this article, free sulfhydryls occur in the fibrillar material throughout the keratinized regions as well as in the precursor epithelium. From the distribution of these chemical groups in snakes' scales, it appears that there is little difference between scales and epidermis except for an extension of a similar process. Yet the former is considered "hard" and the latter "soft."

The distribution of sulfhydryl and disulfides in mature feathers (remiges and pennae) was quite different from that in hairs. Cross sections taken through the quill or calamus that lies in the dermal follicle and through the proximal and distal parts of the shaft or rachis of the vane in the exposed part of the feather were very strongly reactive for sulfhydryls (Fig. 17) and also positive for disulfides. The pith enclosed within the quill showed a negligible reaction for sulfhydryls but an intense reaction for disulfides. Since all portions of the shaft showed a strong reaction for sulfhydryl groups, no keratogenous zone comparable with that in hair could be found. The outer portions of filiplumes (hair feathers) and down reacted more like mammalian hair in that they contained few sulfhydryls but were strongly reactive for disulfides (Figs. 19 and 20).

The beaks of ducks presented another modification of stratified squamous epithelium in which the outer fully cornified portion (stratum corneum) was more reactive for sulfhydryls than the inner stratified epithelium (stratum Malpighii). Both zones, especially the outer one, contained disulfides (Figs. 15 and 16). Again, there was a close similarity of the results obtained with these structures to those of thick epidermis and to snake scales.

Finally in emphasis of the occurrence of free sulfhydryls as well as disulfides as being widespread in fully keratinized structures were the findings in porcupine quills, rhinoceros horn (Fig. 18), and hoof as well as pangolin scales. Indeed, examining the entire group of tissues that could be called "hard" keratins, the distribution of sulfhydryls and disulfides could only be called heterogeneous in comparison with the distribution in hair.

The distribution of sulfhydryls and disulfides in the epidermis has been used frequently as a model for soft keratin (Giroud and Leblond, 1951). In the skin of rodents and other mammals the entire stratum corneum and the stratum granulosum was positive for sulfhydryls (Fig. 10). The outer layers were usually slightly less reactive than the inner ones. However, in some specimens (seen occasionally in mouse, rat, hamster, and in deer, guinea pig, armadillo, and human) there was an intensely reactive zone between the stratum granulosum and the stratum corneum (Fig. 10). This would correspond to the previously described keratogenous zone which supposedly occurs in only hard keratin (Giroud and Leblond, 1951). The transitional zone in epidermis which stains poorly in histological preparations does not exist histochemically; that is, there is no zone where the histochemical reaction appeared to be masked (Fig. 11).

Disulfide groups occurred throughout the epidermis (Fig. 11). It should be stressed that these groups were present in the stratum basalis and other regions of the Malpighian layer and were not restricted to the stratum corneum although there was concentration of disulfides in that region. Keratohyaline granules contained neither sulfhydryls nor disulfides.

A few miscellaneous regions remain to be discussed—the medulla and root sheaths of hair as well as other stratified squamous epithelia. The cells of the medulla of hairs show a moderate reaction for sulfhydryls but no disulfides (Fig. 1). The outer root sheath is positive for sulfhydryls and disulfides throughout its entire length. In the inner sheath, Henle's layer is more strongly reactive than Huxley's layer, especially in the lower portion of the hair (Fig. 5). Trichohyaline granules are unreactive, as are the cells of the cuticle of the inner sheath.

Other stratified squamous epithelium (lip, tongue, oral mucosa, esophagus, vagina, and cornea) show a distribution of sulfhydryls

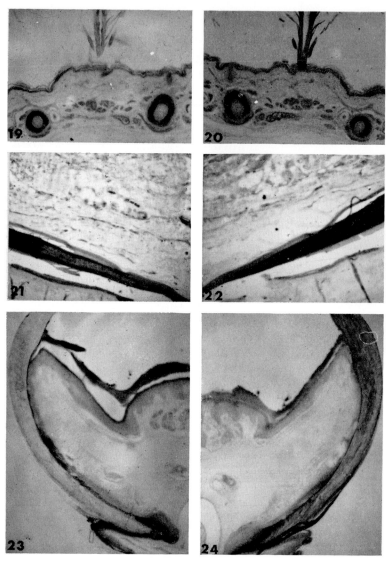

Figs. 19 and 20.   Sections of skin of duck showing several feather follicles in the dermis and distal portion of a feather above the epidermis. The proximal portion of the feather is reactive for sulfhydryls (Fig. 19) whereas the distal portion of the feather contains both sulfhydryls (Fig. 19) and disulfides (Fig. 20) (×28).

and disulfides similar to that of the epidermis. Although the distribution of these groups in the vaginal epithelium of rats appears to vary with different stages of the vaginal cycle (Bern *et al.*, 1957), there are enough morphological and histochemical similarities to assume that keratinization occurs as a normal process in this organ. Similar reactions were found with the esophageal and buccal mucosa, epithelia which are rich in sulfhydryls with intensification of the reaction just above the stratum granulosum (Fig. 12). This point may have some significance because of similar findings in some specimens of epidermis.

Finally, the young enamel matrix has long been known to exhibit similar histological staining reactions to those seen in the stratified squamous epithelium lining of the mouth from which the enamel-forming cells originate. With the specific reactions studied here, the young enamel matrix reacts of faintly few sulfhydryl groups, less than any other epithelial derivative. An even weaker reaction for disulfides occurred in the mature enamel. These weak reactions are in keeping with the low cystine content and the low degree of birefringence (Sognnaes, 1955). On this basis the above reactions may be due to other proteins than keratins.

Discussion

Several points become clear as a result of this comparative investigation of the distribution of sulfhydryls and disulfides in vertebrate keratins. Most fully keratinized tissues with the major exception of the distal portion of the hair shaft contain some free sulfhydryl groups, and not all these groups are oxidized to disulfides in the process of keratinization. Some of the regions concerned with the formation of fibrous keratins appear to contain disulfides in addi-

---

Figs. 21 and 22.   Sections through the proximal tip of a human finger nail. Figure 21 indicates that the cellular matrix at the proximal portion of the fully formed nail is positive for sulfhydryls as well as the superficial and deep stratum of the nail. All zones of the nail contain disulfides (Fig. 22) (×28).

Figs. 23 and 24.   Sections through the claw of a mouse. The matrix of the claw (bottom) is rich in sulfhydryls (Fig. 23), but some weakly reactive fibrils are also present in the distal portion. Most, if not all, of the disulfides are present in the distal portion (Fig. 24).

tion to sulfhydryls. These findings are indicative that many of the previous distinctions between hard and soft keratins do not hold up when investigated with newer and more specific methods. Among the pertinent findings leading to the conclusion are:

1. The epidermis sometimes shows a sulfhydryl-rich keratogenous zone that is supposed to occur only in hard keratins. Furthermore, parakeratotic membranes as found in the buccal cavity, the esophagus, and the vagina show a similar reaction.

2. The stratum corneum, which has been considered the fully keratinized zone, contains free sulfhydryls. The stratum Malpighii which contains obvious birefringent fibrils, even in the basal layers, has disulfides as well as sulfhydryls which appear localized with phase microscopy primarily in the fibrils (Barrnett and Seligman, 1954; Van Scott and Flesch, 1954).

3. In the epidermis that does not show a keratogenous zone, there appears to be a direct histochemical transformation of the sulfhydryl and disulfide positive material from the stratum Malpighii to the cornified layers. This gradual transition is supposed to be diagnostic of hard keratins (Giroud and Leblond, 1951).

4. Keratohyaline granules contain neither sulfhydryls nor disulfides, and so from a histochemical point of view appear to have nothing to do with the process of keratinization as previously implied (Favre, 1950). The same hold true for the isotropic trichohyaline granules (Branca, 1911) of the root sheath of hairs.

5. The medulla (Giroud and Bulliard, 1930) and inner root sheath of hairs (Branca, 1911) have been referred to as soft keratins, and in neither instance may keratin be present. The medulla, although weakly positive for sulfhydryls, contains no disulfides. Part of the difficulty with these derivatives of stratified squamous epithelium is the frequent misuse of the word keratinization for cornification. Despite the attempt at clarification of these terms by Bekker and King (1931), thirty years ago, the significance of these terms is still diluted by abuse.

6. Most hard keratogenous tissues like nail, claw, feather, horn, or scale which have not been widely investigated necessarily do not contain a histochemical keratogenous zone (Giroud and Le-

blond, 1951), as exemplified in hair, but rather the reaction appeared as a direct transition from the sulfhydryl-positive fibrils in the germinative layers to the horny distal regions of the structures which contain both sulfhydryls and disulfides. However, the direct transition of fibrillar material appeared to occur histochemically in all varieties of keratogenous material including the soft epidermis, the findings of which were quite similar to some hard structures like scales and beaks.

This evidence indicates that division of keratins into hard and soft varieties on a histochemical basis (Giroud *et al.*, 1934; Giroud and Leblond, 1951), is an oversimplification of the facts, and this has been pointed out by a variety of works (Barrnett, 1953, 1955; Barrnett and Seligman, 1954; Eisen *et al.*, 1953; Hardy, 1952; Lapiere, 1947; Mescon and Flesch, 1952; Matoltsy, 1958; Montagna, 1956; Van Scott and Flesch, 1954). On physical and histological bases, this division may be more sound. As more knowledge is gathered concerning these fibrous proteins, it appears that they are chemically a heterogeneous group of homologous proteins—more heterogeneous than other homologous proteins, such as elastin, collagen, and hemoglobin. In each instance histochemical aspects of the process of keratinization appears as dissimilar, even among the hard keratins from lamprey teeth to scales or feathers to hair, as suggested difference between epidermis and hair. For these reasons we believe that keratogenous tissues should be specifically named as to the type of tissue and the animal in which they are found.

The common denominator that we have repeatedly found in this investigation was the production of a fibrillar protein in the matrix cells of the epidermis or epidermal derivatives. This fibrous material contains either sulfhydryl groups or disulfide groups or both. The formation, content, and subsequent fate of these proteins is probably characteristic for each individual keratin though similarities overlap and probably exist.

Acknowledgment. The authors are indebted to Dr. Charles P. Lyman of the Museum of Comparative Zoology, Harvard University, whose efforts in providing specimens of numerous ectodermal derivatives gave greater breadth to their sampling of the vertebrate keratins.

REFERENCES

Astbury, W. T. 1933. X-ray interpretation of fiber structure. *Science Progr.*, 28: 210–228.

Astbury, W. T., and Woods, H. J. 1930. X-ray interpretation of the structure and elastic properties of hair keratin. *Nature*, 126: 913–914.

Barrnett, R. J. 1953. The histochemical distribution of protein bound sulfhydryl groups. *J. Natl. Cancer Inst.*, 13: 905–925.

Barrnett, R. J. 1955. Sulfhydryl and disulfide groups of protein. *Texas Repts. Biol. and Med.*, 3: 611–622.

Barrnett, R. J., and Seligman, A. M. 1952. Histochemical demonstration of protein-bound sulfhydryl groups. *Science*, 116: 323–327.

Barrnett, R. J., and Seligman, A. M. 1954. Histochemical demonstration of sulfhydryl and disulfide groups of protein. *J. Natl. Cancer Inst.*, 14: 769–792.

Barrnett, R. J., and Sognnaes, R. F. 1955. Histochemical investigation of sulfhydryl and disulfide groups in keratinous tissues. (Abs.) *Anat. Record*, 121: 260.

Barrnett, R. J., Tsou, K. C., and Seligman, A. M. 1955. Further histochemical characterization of protein-bound sulfhydryl groups: The use of naphthol-containing, mercaptide-forming and alkylating compounds as reagents. *J. Histochem. and Cytochem.*, 3: 406–408.

Bekker, J. G., and King, A. J. 1931. Sulphur distribution in the component structures of wool and porcupine quills. *Biochem. J.*, 25: 1077–1080.

Bern, H. A., Alfert, M., and Blair, S. M. 1957. Cytochemical studies of keratin formation and of epithelial metaplasia in the rodent vagina and prostate. *J. Histochem. and Cytochem.*, 5: 105–119.

Block, R. J., and Vickery, H. B. 1931. The basic amino acids of proteins: A chemical relationship between various keratins. *J. Biol. Chem.*, 93: 113–117.

Branca, A. 1911. Recherches sur la keratinisation: Sur la structure du poil. *J. de l'anat.*, 47: 545–600.

Chevremont, M., and Frederic, J. 1943. Une nouvelle methode histochimeque de mise en evidence des substances à fonction sulfhydrile. *Arch. biol. (Liége)*, 54: 589–605.

Eisen, A. Z., Montagna, W., and Chase, B. 1953. Sulfhydryl groups in the skin of the mouse and guinea pig. *J. Natl. Cancer Inst.*, 14: 341–354.

Favre, M. 1950. Le chondriome de l'epiderme normal et des epidermes pathologiques ortho- et parakératinisations. *Ann. dermatol. syphilig.*, 10: 241–262.

Giroud, A., Bulliard, H. 1930. La kératinisation de l'épiderme et de phanères. Genèse des substances soufrées de la keratins. *Arch. morphol. gen. et exptl.*, 29: 1–83.

Giroud, A., Bulliard, H., and Leblond, C. P. 1934. Les deux types fonda-mentaux de kératinisation. *Bull. histol. appl. physiol. et pathol. et tech. microscop.*, *11*: 129–144.

Giroud, A., and Leblond, C. P. 1951. The keratinization of epidermis and its derivatives, especially the hair, as shown by x-ray diffraction and histochemical studies. *Ann. N.Y. Acad. Sci.*, *53*: 613–626.

Hardy, M. H. 1952. The histochemistry of hair follicles in the mouse. *Am. J. Anat.*, *90*: 285–337.

Lapiere, M. S. 1947. Les substance à fonction sulfhydryle dans la peau normale et dans divers états pathologiques cutanes. *Ann. dermatol. syphilig.*, *3*: 176–178.

Matoltsy, A. G. 1958. The chemistry of keratinization. In *The Biology of Hair Growth*, W. Montagna and R. A. Ellis, Editors. Academic Press, New York.

Mescon, H., and Flesch, P. 1952. Modification of Bennett's method for the histochemical demonstration of free sulfhydryl groups in skin. *J. Invest. Dermatol.*, *18*: 261–266.

Montagna, W. 1956. *The Structure and Function of Skin.* Academic Press, New York.

Percival, G. H., and Steward, C. P. 1930. On the sulphydryl-containing constituent of the epidermis and its relationship to melanogenesis and keratinization. *Brit. J. Dermatol. Syphills*, *42*: 215–229.

Seligman, A. M., Tsou, K. C., and Barrnett, R. J. 1954. A new histochemi-cal method for the demonstration of protein bound sulfhydryl groups with 4-hydroxy-l-naphthyl-N-maleimide. *J. Histochem. and Cyto-chem.*, *2*: 434–444.

Sognnaes, R. F. 1955. Microstructure and histochemical characteristics of the mineralized tissues. *Ann. N.Y. Acad. Sci.*, *60*: 545–574.

Sognnaes, R. F., and Lustig, L. 1955. Histochemical reactions of the lam-prey mouth. *J. Dent. Research*, *34*: 132–143.

Stoves, J. L. 1947. Some biological and chemical properties of animal hair. *J. Soc. Dyers Colourists*, *63*: 65–77.

Tsou, K. C., Barrnett, R. J., and Seligman, A. M. 1955. Preparation of some N-(1-naphthyl)-maleimides as sulfhydryl group reagents. *J. Am. Chem. Soc.*, *77*: 4613–4616.

Unna, P. G., and Golodetz, L. 1909. Die Hautfette. *Biochem. Z.*, *20*: 469–502.

Van Scott, E. J., and Flesch, P. 1954. Sulfhydryl and disulfide in keratin-ization. *Science*, *119*: 70–71.

Wilkerson, V. A. 1934. The chemistry of human epidermis. I. Amino acid content of the stratum corneum and its comparison to other human keratins. *J. Biol. Chem.*, *107*: 377–381.

3

Cultivation of Skin, Pure Epidermal Sheets, and Tooth Germs in vitro*

WITH A NOTE ON THE EFFECT OF VITAMIN A

GEORGE SZABÓ

Department of Dermatology, Massachusetts General Hospital, Harvard Medical School, Boston, Massachusetts

The basal cell of ectodermal epithelia differentiates into more than one cell type. When there is no obvious inductive association with mesenchymal elements, it becomes either the keratinizing Malpighian cell of the epidermis of the skin or the epithelium of the oral mucosa; or it may develop into a sebaceous cell or may form various portions of the sweat gland complex. When this ectodermal basal cell is closely associated with mesenchymal cells during development, two types of differentiation occur. In skin it forms the hair matrix of the hair bulb and this, in turn, gives rise to the intricate epithelial structure of the outer and inner root sheaths and other epithelial elements of the hair follicle. In oral epithelium the basal cell forms another complicated epithelial structure, the enamel organ of the tooth germ. The basal cell in the hair matrix undergoes a strictly regulated periodic cycle of rest and growth, lasting throughout the life of the individual, unless irreversible changes

* This investigation was supported in part by a U.S. Public Health Service Research Grant C-3776 (C) and in part by a research grant of the London Hospital, England.

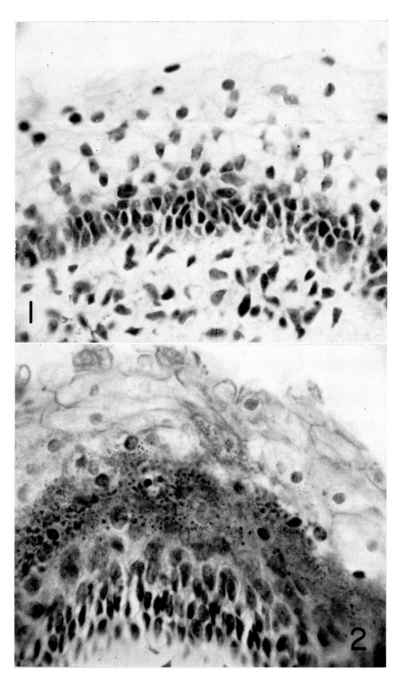

cause degeneration of the hair matrix. In contrast, the life span of the enamel organ is ephemeral, and the cells disappear after having laid down the enamel matrix and shaped the root of the tooth. Only the epithelial rests of Malassez survive in adult life, scattered around the roots of erupted teeth.

The present discussion will deal with several of the cell variants by comparing their behavior *in vitro*. Particular attention will be paid to the differences in cell behavior attributable to the age of the donor, to the composition of the culture medium, and to the tissue composition of the organ cultures.

Materials and Methods

Tooth germs or erupted incisor teeth of mice were maintained as organ cultures in fluid medium, consisting of equal parts of mammalian serum, embryo extract and Pannett and Compton saline (Szabó, 1954). Skin explants were maintained in a variety of media, ranging from the same medium described above, to the completely synthetic medium of Parker 1066, supplied by Connaught Research Laboratories (Szabó, unpublished). Skin from human fetuses, babies, or adults were cultured either as intact dermo-epidermal explants, or the epidermis was separated from the dermis by the skin-splitting technique of Medawar (1941) using a 0.5% solution of commercial trypsin in a normal saline solution, buffered by 0.05% sodium bicarbonate. The trypsin was allowed to act upon thin shavings of the skin for about 20 to 30 minutes at 37°C.

In the study of the effect of vitamin A on epidermal basal cells, Vitamin A-Alkohol (Hoffmann-La Roche) was incorporated into the medium, the final concentration varying between 1500–4500 international units (IU) per 100 ml of medium (Fell and Mellanby, 1953; Szabó unpublished). The explants were embedded and sectioned in the usual way.

Fig. 1. Fetal skin (3 in.), finger. Hematoxylin and eosin, ×800. Control to Fig. 2. No stratum granulosum.

Fig. 2. Section through a skin explant from corresponding finger, as shown in Fig. 1, cultured for 9 days in normal medium. Masson trichrome stain, ×800. Note the well-developed stratum granulosum.

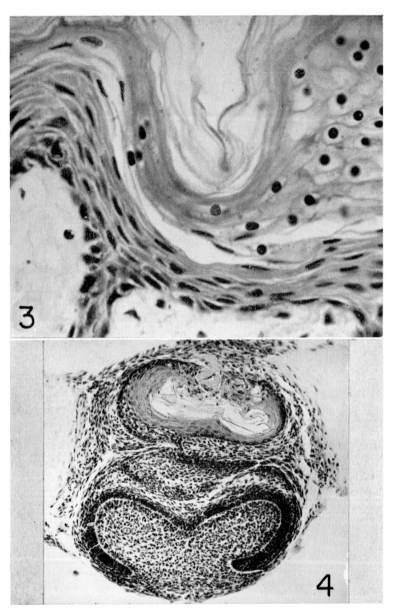

Fig. 3. Adult skin from the abdomen, cultured for 5 days in normal medium. Masson trichrome stain, ×800. Almost normal keratinization seen on the left half of the explant; nuclei, however, are basophilic in the stratum lucidum. On the right half there is a large area of typical swollen cells, with pyknotic nuclei and a cellular structure similar to the upper epidermis shown in Fig. 1.

Results

Cultures without Additional Vitamin A

Comparison of Keratinization of Embryonic and Adult Human Skin in Normal Media

There is a great contrast in the behavior of organ cultures of skin in regard to the age of the donor. Fetal skin undergoes a rapid keratinization *in vitro,* starting at a stage when no keratohyalin granules were formed at the time of explanation (Figs. 1 and 2). After eight days *in vitro* a stratum granulosum has developed (Fig. 2).

Adult skin, however, behaves differently (Fig. 3). Keratinization proceeds normally only in some regions. Even in these regions there are basophilic nuclei in the stratum lucidum. In the majority of cultures the adult epidermis becomes somewhat similar to normal fetal skin (shown in Fig. 1) or to vaginal epithelium. The layers above the stratum basale become less basophilic, the nuclei are pycnotic, and the cytoplasm is vacuolated. The stratum granulosum, formed *in vivo* prior to explantation, may remain unchanged for several days, and formation of new granular layer is doubtful. Finally, the skin explants lose most of the epidermis as the basal cells migrate along the basement membrane and form a thin epithelial layer which surrounds the whole explant (Fig. 11).

Behavior of Pure Epidermal Sheets from Adult Skin

Pure epidermal sheets behave in a similar fashion to adult epidermis (Figs. 5 and 6), with the exception that, in the absence of dermis as a substrate, the migrating epidermal cells encyst the epidermis itself. There is a tendency to form pearl-like dyskeratotic epithelial nests in a larger number than in whole skin explants.

Epidermal melanocytes (cf. Billingham, 1948; Szabó, 1959) preserve their cellular identity *in vitro.* They are distinguishable by

---

Fig. 4. Section through a first molar germ of mouse, 17th day *in utero,* 5 days *in vitro.* Harris's hematoxylin, eosin ×160. A keratinizing cyst, derived from the oral epithelium, is over the normally developing tooth germ. (Szabó, 1954; reproduced by permission of Cambridge University Press.)

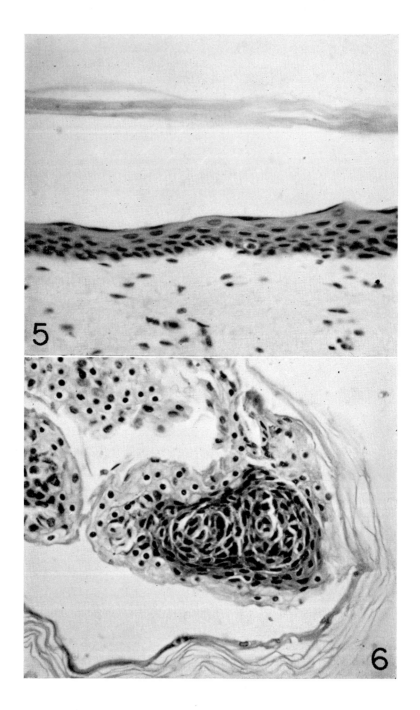

their affinity to dopa. They lose their characteristic dendritic shape within the first three to five days and become spindle-shaped with two principal dendrites extended parallel to the plane of the basement membrane. They behave in the same fashion in pure epidermal explants, where they often occupy a central position in the epithelial nests.

Behavior of the Basal Cell of the Enamel Organ in vitro

When tooth germs of molar teeth of mice are maintained in organ cultures (Fig. 4), the morphogenetic development of the enamel organ continues. The epithelial sheet of Hertwig is growing downward, enclosing the dental papilla, and all four layers of the enamel organ develop normally. In the same cultures the basal layer of the gingiva, however, forms keratinized cysts (Fig. 4).

In cultures of the enamel organ of the continuously growing incisor teeth (Figs. 7 and 8), the formation of the enamel matrix may continue ectopically (Fig. 7). In cultures older than ten days, (Fig. 8, 2 weeks) the enamel epithelium is transformed into stratified squamous epithelium with a basal layer nearest to the free surface of the explant.

Behavior of Glandular Derivates of the Epidermis in vitro

The sebaceous glands degenerate rapidly in organ cultures, whereas isolated sebaceous cells in a cell suspension remain viable for three to five weeks, as judged by the intact appearance of the cells (Szabó, unpublished).

The duct portion of sweat glands is not identifiable in the cultures older than five days, as the epithelial cells of the root sheaths of hair follicles and the cells of the sweat ducts migrate toward the free surfaces of the explant and partake in the formation of the encysting epithelial lining of the cultured skin. The glandular portions of the

---

Fig. 5.   Section through normal skin, breast. Hematoxylin and eosin, ×480. Control to Fig. 6. The split between the stratum granulosum and keratin layer is an artifact.

Fig. 6.   Culture of pure epidermal sheet, 3 days in vitro. Hematoxylin and eosin, ×480. Pearl-like epithelial islands formed in the bay of keratin formed prior to explantation.

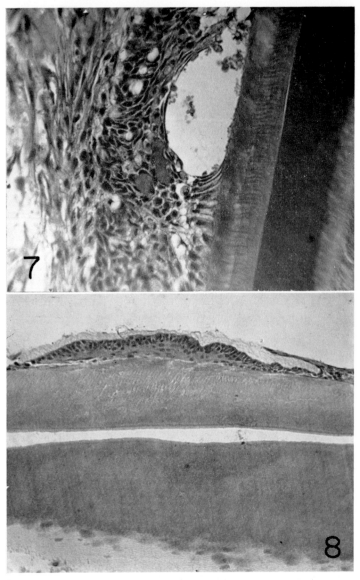

Fig. 7. Enamel organ of an erupted incisor tooth, cultured under high O_2 tension for 8 days. Weigert-van Gieson ×400. Note the ectopic enamel matrix (and enamel?) around the cyst between the enamel matrix proper and the enamal organ. Enamel matrix hypoplastic. (Szabó, 1954; reproduced by permission of Cambridge University Press.)

Fig. 8. Enamel organ of an erupted incisor, cultured for 14 days. Harris's hematoxylin eosin, ×200. Stratified squamous epithelium over the enamel matrix, formed from the enamel organ *in vitro*. (Szabó, 1954; reproduced by permission of Cambridge University Press.)

sweat ducts, however, preserve their original structure as long as the cultures are maintained (three to four weeks).

Keratinization of Hair Follicles in vitro

Hair follicles were seldom included in the skin explants, as the density of hair follicles is very low in human skin, especially in the regions where biopsy specimens were obtained (thigh, foreskin; Szabó, 1958). The matrix of the hair follicles resembles the glandular portion of the sweat glands in the sense that it remains viable as long as cultures are maintained. Keratinization of newly forming hairs was not observed. Epithelial "pearls" form also inside the hair matrix. Cells of the matrix take part in the encystment of the explant.

EFFECT OF VITAMIN A ON ADULT SKIN

Vitamin A has a general "promoting effect" on the growth of the epidermis. Figures 11 and 12 compare fourteen-day-old cultures without and with vitamin A in the medium. The epidermis in Fig. 11 without vitamin A is much thinner than the epidermis in Fig. 12 (2 to 5 cell layers in comparison to 15 to 20 layers). Furthermore, the nuclei in the control culture are degenerate and often resemble empty shells, and the cytoplasm is fibrillar, whereas the nuclei in the vitamin A cultures are normal.

Vitamin A has another specific effect on the basal cells. Figures 9 and 10 compare basal cells of the epidermis before and after culturing in a medium containing 1500 IU of vitamin A per 100 ml of medium, for seven days, whereas Fig. 3 shows a culture in normal medium, without vitamin A. The cuboidal or columnar cells in the basal layer of the epidermis of the biopsy (Fig. 9) became flattened in the control culture (Fig. 3). In the culture with vitamin A, however, the basal layer became highly columnar at places with a characteristic, shallow, alveolar-like undulation of the basal layer. The nuclei of these basal cells are usually pushed to the opposite end, away from the basement membrane. These areas of highly columnar basal cells are connected with a row of low columnar cells. A melanocyte with a darkly stained nucleus is also shown in Fig. 9. The suprabasal position of this melanocyte is unusual; the shape

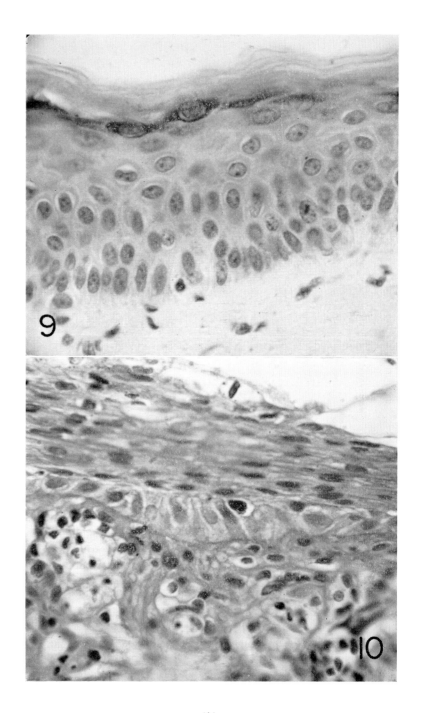

and size of the cell, however, is normal, resembling a characteristic "clear cell." The cell layers above the basal layer resemble those shown in Fig. 12. Parakeratosis is almost entirely absent.

Vitamin A in concentrations higher than 1500 IU per 100 ml of medium did not produce greater or more consequent changes.

Parakeratosis was also absent in the long-term cultures similar to that shown in Fig. 12.

Vitamin A did not have an effect on sebaceous glands as they degenerated just as rapidly as in the controls. The effect of vitamin A on the keratinization of hairs is still to be observed on explants derived from regions more hairy than those included in the present study.

Discussion

The most important result of this study is that there is a basic difference between the embryonic and adult basal cells of the epidermis regarding their behavior *in vitro*. Basal cells are self-differentiating when explanted in an embryonic stage. Basal cells of adult epidermis, however, are not self-differentiating and show pycnotic degeneration or dyskeratosis *in vitro*. Confusion arose in the past because no clear distinction was made between the fate of embryonic skin cultures and the behavior of explants of adult skin. The fate of organ cultures of adult skin were aptly described in the classical paper of Pinkus (1939) and more recently by Medawar (1948). The majority of investigators, however, based their studies of keratinization *in vitro* on explanted embryonic skin (Drew, 1922, mouse; Chlopin, 1932, human; Miszursky, 1937, chicken; Litvac, 1939, chicken; and Hanson, 1950, rodent). Even in these cases, as

---

Fig. 9.   Thigh skin, control to Figs. 10–12. Hematoxylin eosin, ×800. Stratum granulosum one cell layer thick; basal layer of epidermis is low columnar-cuboidal.

Fig. 10.   Skin cultured in a medium containing vitamin A (1500 IU per 100 ml of medium) for 7 days. Mallory trichrome stain, ×800. Note the tall columnar cells in the basal layer and the dark nucleus of a melanocyte at the top of this layer; the cells of the superficial epidermis are flat and parallel to the surface. No stratum granulosum, no keratinization, no pycnosis of nuclei (cf. Fig. 3).

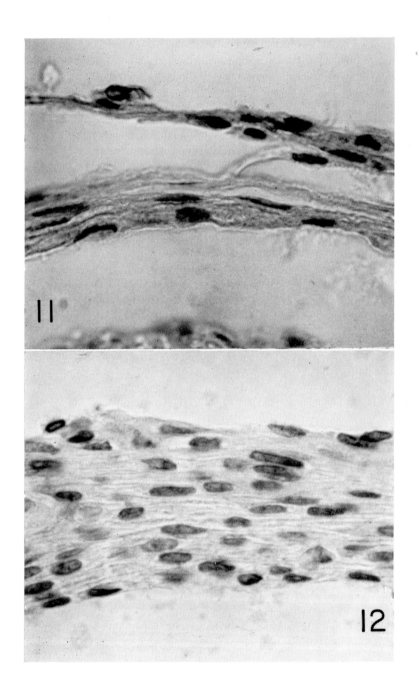

Pinkus (1939) pointed out, we are not dealing with true keratinization but with dyskeratosis.

The failure of the adult epidermis to produce keratinization under the same conditions that an embryonic epithelium would indicates that the commonly used tissue culture media are not lacking in any factor necessary for the onset of keratinization. The adult basal cells of the epidermis, therefore, may be different from the basal cells of the prospective ectoderm; furthermore, the tissue culture environment in general is unfavorable for a continued keratinization of adult skin. The lack of dehydration at the skin surface and the absence of any friction and the presence of "chronic wound healing" conditions come to mind as obvious factors. Nutritional changes due to explantation and to a rich supply of nutrients in the media may also interfere with keratinization, whereas, according to Drew (1922), "starvation" of cultures promotes keratinization. On the other hand, in the embryo, the physical environment is similar to that of the tissue culture. Adult skin epidermis is transformed to an epithelium *in vitro,* which is somewhat similar to normal embryonic epithelium before keratinization takes place (cf. Figs. 1 and 3).

It was debated for some time whether the presence of connective tissue is essential for keratinization. Drew (1923) thought that it is essential; whereas Fischer (1924) found that cultures of pure epithelial cells derived from the iris of chick embryos keratinize. Our experiments with cultures of pure ectodermal epithelium suggest that keratinization (or dyskeratosis) is possible without any connective tissue present in the cultures. When dermis is also included in the cultures, however, normal keratinization may occur in adult skin.

Our findings regarding the derivates of the basal cells agree with the results of others. Pinkus (1939) also found that the epithelium of sweat glands survives as long as two months *in vitro.* Medawar

Fig. 11. Skin cultured in normal medium for 14 days. Hematoxylin eosin, ×800. Narrow epidermis, pyknotic nuclei, highly refractile cytoplasm.

Fig. 12. Skin cultured in a medium containing vitamin A (3000 IU per 100 ml medium) for 14 days. Hematoxylin eosin, ×800. Healthy epidermis, much thicker than in Fig. 11, normal nuclei. No keratinization. Separation from dermis in Figs. 11 and 12 is an artifact.

(1948), however, described healthy sebaceous glands in his cultures, although these glands degenerated rapidly in our cultures. It is possible that the high O_2 content of the atmosphere in his cultures enhanced the survival of these cells. Our finding that sebaceous cells survive when they are isolated suggests that these cells are not hypersensitive to the changed environment *in vitro* under all conditions, but may be at a disadvantage when embalmed *in situ* in organ cultures.

Past observations on hair growth *in vitro* also have been made on embryonic material (Strangeways, 1931; Hardy, 1949). In Medawar's experiments (1948) the cells of the root sheaths took part in the encystment of the explant in much the same way as in our case. More experiments involving explanted skin from areas with dense hair follicle population are needed for a study of changes in the hair cycle *in vitro* of the adult skin.

The most interesting results in recent years in the field of skin tissue culture are those of Fell and Mellanby (1953), who demonstrated that vitamin A has a metaplastic effect on the prospective ectoderm of chicken explants. For a further discussion of this effect we refer here to the papers in this volume of Bern and Lawrence and Parnell and Sherman. Our experiments show that vitamin A has a profound effect on adult human epidermis *in vitro;* a transformation of the basal cells into ciliated mucous cells, however, has not yet been observed. It would be very interesting to determine if vitamin A has a morphogenetic effect *in vivo.* It is possible that cells of the epithelial lining of the gastro-intestinal tract and the respiratory system have a lower threshold to vitamin A than the basal cells of the prospective epidermis as they develop into mucous cells *in vivo,* whereas the epidermis becomes keratinized. Vitamin A is a chemically defined agent possessing a distinct morphological effect.

The behavior of tooth germs *in vitro* has been described by Glasstone (1938) and by the present author (Szabó, 1954). It should be pointed out that under identical conditions the basal cells of the embryonic gingival epithelium keratinize, whereas the basal cells which produce the enamel organ initiate the formation of dentine and later form enamel. The fate of vitamin A on enamel organs has not been adequately studied.

Summary

1. Basal cells of the embryonic ectodermal derivates are self-differentiating *in vitro:* epidermis keratinizes; the enamel epithelium forms enamel matrix.

2. Under identical conditions, embryonic skin keratinizes (self-differentiates), whereas adult skin usually stops keratinizing and shows dyskeratotic changes.

3. Cultures of pure ectodermal epithelium from adult skin behave similarly to whole skin cultures, as they also show dyskeratotic changes. Connective tissue, therefore, is not essential for dyskeratosis.

4. Vitamin A, in addition to its general hyperplastic effect on epidermis, also has a special effect in that it inhibits keratinization (or dyskeratosis) and induces a metaplasia in the basal layer; the basal cells become highly columnar, whereas no mucin formation has been observed. It has no effect on the behavior of sweat glands and sebaceous glands *in vitro.*

Acknowledgment. The author wishes to express his gratitude to Professor P. B. Medawar, Dr. B. F. Russell, and Dr. Geoffrey H. Bourne for their continuous help during this investigation. Hoffmann-La Roche, Inc., has generously supplied the vitamin A samples.

REFERENCES

Billingham, R. E. 1948. Dendritic cells. *J. Anat.,* 28: 93–109.

Chlopin, N. G. 1932. Über einige Wachstums- und Differentierungserscheinungen an der embryonalen menschlichen Epidermis im Explantat. *Wilhelm Roux, Arch. Entwicklungsmech. Organ.,* 126: 69–89.

Drew, A. H. 1922. A comparative study of normal and malignant tissues grown in artificial culture. *Brit. J. Exptl. Pathol.,* 3: 20–27.

Drew, A. H. 1923. Three lectures on the cultivation of tissues and tumours *in vitro. Lancet,* 204: 785–787, 833–835.

Fell, H. B., and Mellanby, E. 1953. Metaplasia produced in cultures of chick ectoderm by high vitamin A. *J. Physiol.* (*London*) 119: 470–488.

Fischer, A. 1924. The differentiation and keratinization of epithelium. *J. Exptl. Med.,* 39: 585–587.

Glasstone, S. 1938. A comparative study of the development *in vivo* and *in vitro* of the rat and rabbit molars. *Proc. Roy. Soc.* (*London*), B126: 315–330.

Hanson, J. 1950. Differentiation of mammalian epidermis in tissue culture. *J. Anat., 84*: 30–31.

Hardy, M. H. 1949. The development of mouse hair *in vitro* with some observations on pigmentation. *J. Anat., 83*: 364–384.

Litvac, A. 1939. Sur la kératinisation epitheliale *in vitro*. *Arch. anat. microscop., 35*: 55–63.

Medawar, P. B. 1941. Sheets of pure epidermal epithelium from human skin. *Nature, 148*: 783.

Medawar, P. B. 1948. The cultivation of adult mammalian skin epithelium *in vitro*. *Quart. J. Microscop. Sci., 89*: 187–196.

Miszursky, B. 1937. Researches on the keratinization of epithelium in tissue cultures. *Arch. exptl. Zellforsch. Gewebezücht., 20*: 122–139.

Pinkus, H. 1939. Notes on structure and biological properties of human epidermis and sweat glands in tissue culture and in the organism. *Arch. exptl. Zellforsch. Gewebezücht., 22*: 47–52.

Strangeways, D. H. 1931. The growth of hair *in vitro*. *Arch. exptl. Zellforsch. Gewebezücht., 11*: 344–345.

Szabó, G. 1954. Studies on the cultivation of teeth *in vitro*. *J. Anat., 88*: 31–44.

Szabó, G. 1958. The regional frequency and distribution of hair follicles in human skin. *The Biology of Hair Growth*, W. Montagna and R. A. Ellis, Editors. Academic Press, New York. Pp. 33–38.

Szabó, G. 1959. Quantitative histological investigations on the melanocyte system of the human epidermis. *Pigment Cell Biology*, M. Gordon, Editor. Academic Press, New York. Pp. 99–125.

4

Ultrastructure of Keratin in Oral Mucosa, Skin, Esophagus, Claw, and Hair

JOHANNES A. G. RHODIN* AND EDWARD J. REITH
Department of Anatomy, New York University School of Medicine, New York City

A relatively large number of investigations with the electron microscope have been carried out on keratinizing tissues. Among these are the works of Selby (1955–1957), Porter (1954), Menefee (1957), Odland (1958, 1960), Brody (1959a,b, 1960), Horstmann and Knoop (1958), and others (Albright, 1960; Barnicot and Birbeck, 1958; Burgos and Wislocki, 1958; Charles and Smiddy, 1957; Clark and Hibbs, 1958; Drochmans, 1960; Fasske and Themann, 1959; Gray et al., 1952; Hibbs and Clark, 1959; Matoltsy and Balsamo, 1955; Ottoson et al., 1953; Pease, 1951, 1952; Pillai et al., 1960; Rogers, 1959; Setälä et al., 1960a,b; Sognnaes and Albright, 1956, 1958; Themann, 1958; Vogel, 1958; Weiss and Ferris, 1954). The most extensive reports thus far have been those of Birbeck and Mercer (1957a,b,c), Birbeck et al. (1956), and Mercer (1958), whose works have included descriptions of skin, feather, and hair.

The preparation of keratinized tissue for observation with the electron microscope presents a number of problems due in large measure to the nature of the final product. Because of this, observations have been to a large extent limited to particular aspects of keratinization. For example, Selby (1955–1957) has elucidated

* Recipient of Investigatorship of the Health Research Council of the City New York under contract No. 1-186.

many features of epithelium related to the early stages of keratinization but has offered less information on the cells related to later stages. On the other hand, Brody (1959a,b, 1960), using resins, had considerable success in examining the final product but had less success in studying the early stages. It is difficult to compare findings made with different methods of preservation for the electron microscope and organize them into a composite picture of keratinizing mechanisms. Much of the difficulty can be avoided by examination of young tissue which is much simpler to prepare and which offers other advantages over adult tissue especially when one makes an attempt to elucidate a sequence of events. Considering the general nature of this meeting, we felt it appropriate to seek tissues which would yield information on basic mechanisms involved in keratinization and then to conduct a survey of several mammalian tissues in order to confirm the observations made in the simple systems. As an example of a simple system, we chose the surface of one-day-old rat tongue and skin. Other tissues included adult rat skin, adult mouse esophagus, one-day-old rat claw, and six-month-old mouse hair. To simplify our system further, we studied only albino animals so that organelles and inclusions related to pigment formation would not cloud those related to keratinization.

In general, we concur with the classification of hard and soft keratin as emphasized by Leblond (1951) and Giroud et al. (1934, 1951). We have not found it appropriate at this time to include the cuticle of the hair in the aforementioned types of keratin, but rather refer to it as amorphous keratin. Information will be presented on the formation and structure of all three. Since the purpose of this paper is to uncover the mechanism of keratinization rather than to describe and compare tissues, our illustrations are, because of limited space, selected from the particular tissue which most advantageously shows the structure we describe.

Materials and Methods

The materials used in this study have been the tongue and skin of one-day-old rats, adult rat skin, adult mouse esophagus, one-day-old rat claw, and six-month-old mouse hair. Osmium tetroxide has been used as a fixative (Palade, 1952; Rhodin, 1954; Sjöstrand, 1953) and methacrylate as an embedding medium (Newman *et al.*, 1949) for specimens prepared for electron microscopy. Thin sections for electron microscopy have been cut with either a Porter-Blum (Servall) microtome or an LKB ultrotome. The Siemens Elmiskop I has been employed in obtaining the electron micrographs. Uranyl acetate has been used to enhance contrast in the pictures at high magnifications.

Results

SOFT KERATIN

Tongue, Skin, and Esophagus

The tongue and skin of one-day-old rats and the esophagus of adult mice have been studied as examples of epithelia which undergo keratinization of the soft type. The mechanism of keratinization is essentially similar in all three of these tissues except that differences in amount of intracellular material occur according to location and functional demands.

Three main cell types are observed in epithelia which undergo soft keratinization: a basal layer, an intermediate group of cells, and the final keratinized cells. These are best seen in a low-power view of one-day-old rat tongue (Fig. 1). Even at such low magnifications, significant differences can be noted between the cell types. The basal layer forms a layer of uninterrupted cells adjacent to the supporting connective tissue. The nuclei appear smaller and denser than those of intermediate cells, and there appear to be more nuclei in the germinal layer than in the intermediate layer. This is due to the relatively small amount of cytoplasm in the cells of the basal layer. As these cells move toward the surface, the amount of cytoplasm increases markedly so there appear to be relatively fewer nuclei. The cytoplasm of the intermediate cells is less dense than is the case with basal cells. Keratinized cells have a dense appearance and are easy to recognize. They have thin profiles suggesting that their contents are greatly consolidated when compared with the underlying intermediate cells. Just under the keratinized cells

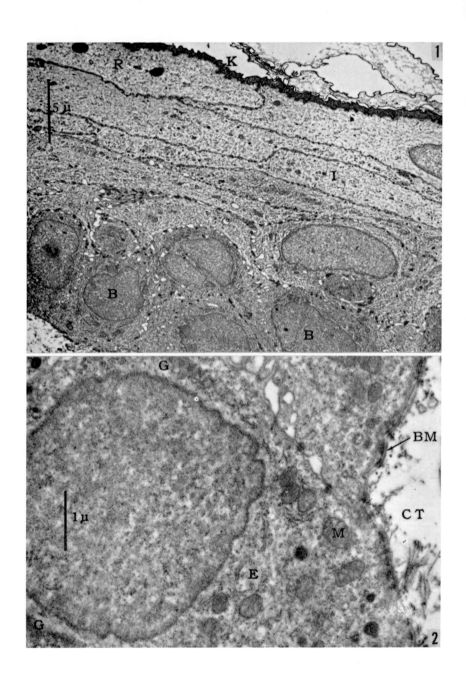

64

are some keratohyalin granules. Beyond the layer of keratinized cells are cells which are partially desquamated. They appear swollen, and when examined with higher magnification, they reveal the same contents as the keratinized cells except that they are less consolidated. Alterations in intercellular space are also noted in such a low-power view; for example, in the basal layer there is a noticeable amount of intercellular space into which microvilli project. This space decreases in amount in the intermediate layer so that none can be observed between the upper cells of the intermediate layer.

The undifferentiated nature of the basal cells is more evident when examined with higher magnification (Fig. 2). The cytoplasm contain small mitochondria randomly scattered throughout the cell and occasional profiles of rough surfaced endoplasmic reticulum. Golgi material is clearly defined; indeed, the indications are that it is reasonably extensive since in some cells more than one aggregate of Golgi material is evident. Small vesicles and submicroscopic ribonucleoprotein (RNP) particles are also present. The remainder of the cytoplasm contains an amorphous, homogeneous material which contributes greatly to the increased density of these cells when they are viewed with lower magnifications.

The basal cells are connected to their neighbors by means of desmosomes. Microvilli extend into the spaces between the cells. A basement membrane lies under the cells forming a thin continuous barrier between the epithelial cells and the connective tissue (Fig. 2). Occasional condensations comparable to desmosomes are seen along the cell membrane which rests on the basement membrane. Where the cell membrane is so condensed, there is frequently a related condensation of the underlying basement membrane.

In the deepest layer of intermediate cells one can already observe

---

Fig. 1.   Survey picture of the epithelium of the tongue of newborn rat. The basal cells (B) have denser cytoplasm than the cells of the intermediate cell layers (I). The fully keratinized layer (K) is greatly consolidated. Several keratohyalin granules (R) are present. At the surface, several sloughed-off cell layers ($\times 3400$).

Fig. 2.   Detail of two basal cells seen in Fig. 1. The basement membrane (BM) borders on the connective tissue space (CT). Mitochondria (M) and elements of rough-surfaced endoplasmic reticulum (E) are seen together with Golgi material (G) ($\times 16,000$).

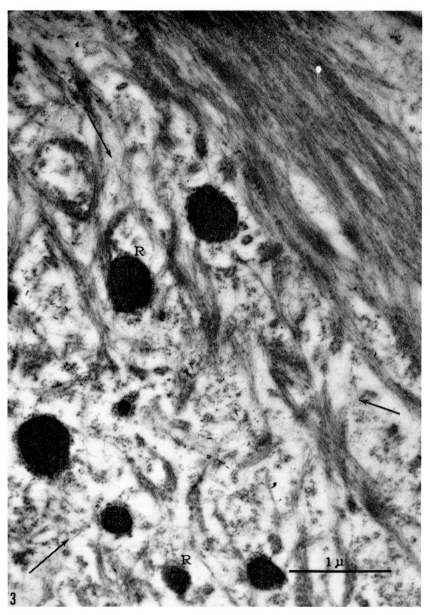

Fig. 3. Detail of a cell in the intermediate cell layers of newborn rat skin. Keratohyalin granules (R) of different sizes are surrounded by RNP particles. Arrows point to narrow single tonofilaments. Wider filaments are grouped and tend to run as parallel pairs for some distance (upper right-hand corner) (×28,000).

intracellular changes directed at keratin formation. Delicate tonofilaments are seen which measure from 30–45 A in width (Fig. 4). These may be seen in a field where thicker tonofilaments are also present. The thicker filaments are about 60–90 A in width. A characteristic irregular beadedness is seen in these tonofilaments. The tonofilaments are placed in a cytoplasmic matrix which appears rather empty, although in the immediate vicinity of the tonofilaments the matrix appears somewhat denser. Rather extensive fields of these tonofilaments are observed without any organelles other than free RNP particles. Nearer the surface, tonofilaments can be seen in the form of bundles which vary in size and length (Fig. 3). The bundles consist of tonofilaments lying side by side in a rather loose manner. There is evidence that these tonofilaments form tubular structures as they increase in thickness from 30–60 A. For example, many neighboring filaments appear as parallel tracks when cut longitudinally. These travel in directions slightly different from other tracks. A number of oval profiles are often observed suggesting that these tonotubules have been cut obliquely. Moreover, a significant number of circular profiles are seen where these tubules have been cut in cross sections. The larger aggregates of tonofilaments measure 2–3 microns in diameter and can be seen with the light microscope, in which case they are referred to as tonofibrils.

After the cells have begun the formation of tonofilaments, and during the lateral growth and aggregation of these filaments, a second component appears which is related to the formation of keratin, namely the keratohyalin granule (Fig. 3). These granules are most numerous and largest under the keratinized layer. When they are sufficiently numerous, the cell layer which contains them is called stratum granulosum. They first appear in cells below this level as small spherical granules surrounded by submicroscopic ribonucleoprotein (RNP) particles. Keratohyalin granules of various size are frequently seen in one cell all with RNP particles surrounding them. Although tonofilaments have been observed in the deepest cells of the intermediate layer, that is, just above the basal layer, keratohyalin granules have not been observed in the deepest intermediate cells.

The largest keratohyalin granules just under the keratinized cells

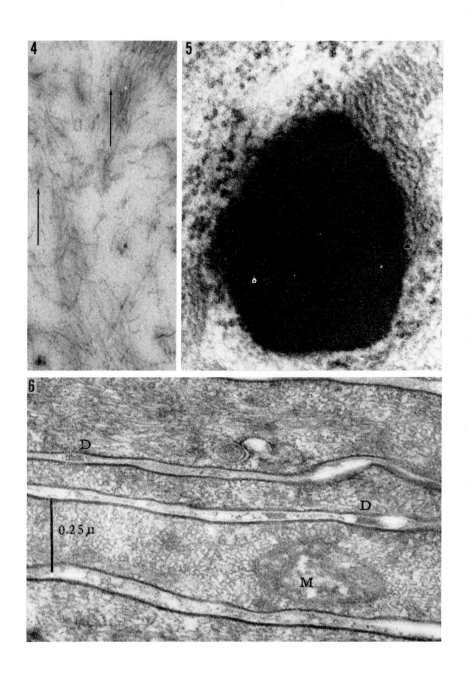

are somewhat irregular in shape (Fig. 5). They still have some RNP particles adjacent to them but now may also have tonofilaments abutting upon them (Figs. 5, 20). This association of keratohyalin granules and tonofilaments occurs only with the largest keratohyalin granules and the widest tonofilaments which have many indications of a tubular structure.

All stages in the development of keratohyalin granules are not always seen in a particular field; therefore, either this occurs rapidly and sporadically or in cycles.

A number of other observations have been made in cells which are undergoing soft keratinization. In the basal cell layer, cell membranes of neighboring cells are not always parallel so that there is an intercellular space into which microvilli project. At numerous places, there are desmosomes which serve as cell contact points. Moving up into the layer of intermediate cells, the amount of intercellular space decreases so that for greater and greater lengths the cell membranes of adjacent cells become parallel. Desmosomes are scattered along the cell membranes (Fig. 17). Upon reaching the uppermost (the most superficial) cells of the intermediate layer, there is only the smallest amount of intercellular space so that adjacent cell membranes are parallel for their entire contact with each other, and no space is left for microvilli. Desmosomes are still scattered along the cell membranes, and toward the surface the size of the desmosomes increases. Moreover, as the surface is approached, the distance between adjacent desmosomes increases and material appears between these cell contact points. The material between desmosomes is organized in the largest spaces so that three layers of dense substance are seen. Indeed, between the parallel cell membranes there is also a dense linear material (Fig. 17). Finally, upon

---

Fig. 4. Detail of the very fine tonofilaments (arrows), measuring 30–45 A in width, as they appear in the deepest intermediate cells of the newborn rat tongue (×62,000).

Fig. 5. Keratohyalin granule in the tongue of newborn rat. In this instance, both RNP particles (left) and obliquely sectioned tonofilaments (right) show a close relation to the keratohyalin granule (×115,000).

Fig. 6. Adult mouse esophagus. Fully keratinized cell layers with irregularly arranged filaments, some form circular profiles. A mitochondrion (M) and remnants of desmosomes (D) are still to be seen (×79,000).

becoming keratinized (Fig. 6), the entire cell membrane becomes significantly thickened and there is no longer any evidence of desmosomes as they were seen in the deeper cells. Between keratinized cells where they are close together, there is seen an opaque material. When the cells are separated slightly, this opaque material is cleaved so that part sticks to the cell membrane of each separating cell.

Rather close to the cell membrane of cells in the intermediate layer are small spherical granules measuring about 0.1 micron in diameter (Fig. 19). When they are examined with higher magnification, they are seen to consist of areas of light and dark staining material enclosed by a distinct outer membrane under which is seen a less well-defined inner membrane. The outer membrane measures about 30 A in width. The inner one is slightly thicker. Irregular extensions occur from the inner membrane into the center of these granules. Although most of the granules are close to the cell membrane, some may be located more deeply within the cell. The size of these granules does not vary much.

Hair Follicle

At this point, it is appropriate to introduce the hair follicle for two reasons. First, it permits us to compare soft keratin formation as described in the above paragraphs with soft keratin formation in the hair; second, the orientation obtained in considering soft keratin of the hair will be useful for subsequent consideration of hard keratin in hair.

A cross section of the growing hair follicle is shown in Fig. 7. The cut was made just above the level of where the cells of Henle's layer became keratinized. By beginning at the outside and working toward the center, the following layers can be recognized:

1. A very thin coat of connective tissue surrounds the entire follicle. The nucleus of a connective tissue cell is seen in the upper left of the figure.

2. Next, there is a rather broad layer of epithelial cells which constitute the cells of the external root sheath. This layer is from one to two cells thick in this figure. These cells do not become keratinized.

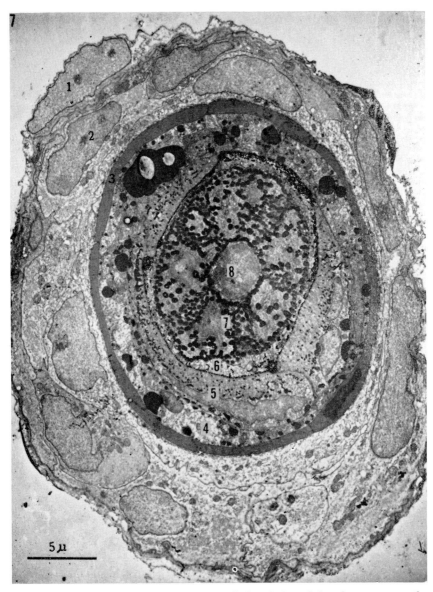

Fig. 7.   Cross-sectioned active hair follicle of the adult white mouse. The layers are: (1) connective tissue, (2) outer root sheath, (3) Henle's layer (keratinized), (4) Huxley's layer, (5) cuticle of inner root sheath, (6) cuticle of the hair, (7) hair cortex, (8) hair medulla (×5500).

71

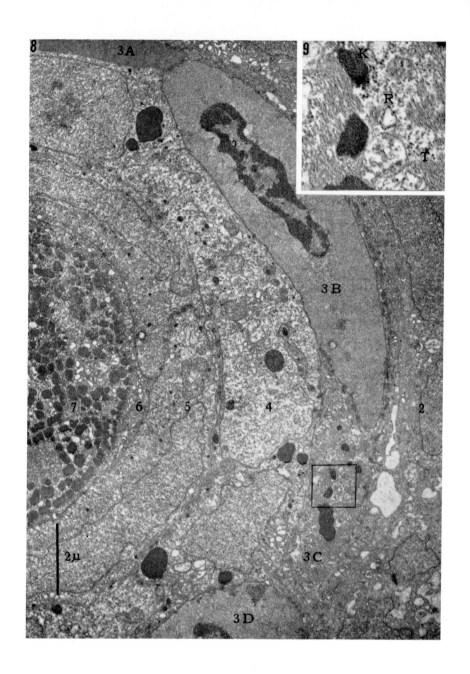

3. Internal to this is a narrow dense cuff of keratinized (soft keratin) cells. These are the cells of Henle's layer, parts of seven cells are noted in this figure. The remains of a nucleus is shown in one of the cells.

4. Deep to Henle's layer is Huxley's layer. These cells are not yet keratinized but will undergo soft keratinization. Numerous keratohyalin (or trichohyalin) granules can be seen in these cells. The largest ones are irregular, the smallest are spherical.

5. The layer deep to this is the cuticle of the inner sheath, and in this low-power view is seen to contain numerous small, spherical trichohyalin granules. This layer also undergoes soft keratinization.

6. The cuticle of the hair cortex is seen next and appears to contain intensely opaque small bodies. The structures of these bodies is not evident in low-magnification views and will be considered below. These cells undergo a type of keratinization which does not compare with the other types described.

7. The cortex of the hair shaft is deep to the cuticle and occupies the center of the cross section. Several nuclei can be seen. The cytoplasm of the cells contains a large number of spherical structures of moderate opacity. When these are examined with higher magnification and in longitudinal sections they are seen to be tonofibrils cut in sections.

8. It is difficult to determine whether the nucleus in the center of the cortex is the nucleus of a cortex cell or the nucleus of a medullary cell.

Of all the layers shown in Fig. 7 only the Henle's layer contained keratinized cells. It is sometimes possible to obtain a section in which cells of Henle are at different stages of keratinization if a sec-

Fig. 8.   Adult mouse hair follicle, cross-sectioned at a lower level than in Fig. 7. Outer root sheath (2), Henle's layer (3), Huxley's layer (4), cuticle of inner root sheath (5), cuticle of hair (6), hair cortex (7). The cells of Henle's layer are in different stages of keratinization. In 3C, trichohyalin granules are still present. In 3B and 3D, keratinization has progressed to a stage where trichohyalin granules are no longer evident, pyknotic nuclei still remain, and the plasma membrane has broadened. In 3A, the keratinization is completed and corresponds to the stage seen in Fig. 7 (×9400).

Fig. 9.   Enlargement of the area squared off in Fig. 8, showing the three main structures participating in soft keratinization: Keratohyalin (trichohyalin) granules (K), RNP particles (R), and tonofilaments (T) (×36,000).

tion (Fig. 8) is taken below the one just described. The uppermost cell is keratinized and is darker than the others. The one below this has just become keratinized, and still retains remnants of a nucleus. Note that the cell membrane of this cell (and of the more fully keratinized cell) is significantly more opaque than the adjacent cell which has not yet become keratinized. In the latter cell, several trichohyalin granules can be seen. The smallest ones are spherical. The larger ones are irregular. In addition to the trichohyalin granules, there are bundles of tonofilaments which fill most of the remaining cytoplasm. When these are examined with higher magnification, they are seen to have the same relationship to trichohyalin (keratohyalin) granules as do the fibers in the tongue (Fig. 9). The close association is evident even in this low magnification. This cell then is equivalent to the cells which would occupy the stratum granulosum of stratified surface epithelium. Note again that the cell membrane of this cell is not nearly as dark as the cell membrane of the cell just above this.

Because of the lower level of this section (Fig. 8), all the features described in Fig. 7 will not be evident. For example, the dark bodies of the cuticle of the cortex have not yet formed and are not seen; the trichohyalin granules of the Huxley's layer are fewer and smaller, and the cuticle of the inner sheath has only a few trichohyalin granules.

The sequence of events leading to keratinization of the Henle's layer, Huxley's layer and the cuticle of the inner sheath is similar to that seen in the simple system; that is, with higher magnification small filaments are seen first; then as they increase in size, number, and organization, small trichohyalin granules appear which become larger during later stages. RNP particles are conspicuously present during both of these events. Then the largest tonofilaments measuring 90 A wide are seen in association with the larger, irregular trichohyalin granules. Finally, there is a dense cell membrane about the keratinized cell and a consolidation of the cell contents (Fig. 18).

As with surface epithelia just prior to the keratinization, the desmosome contact areas increase significantly, and there appears between the cells a three-layered structure (Fig. 18).

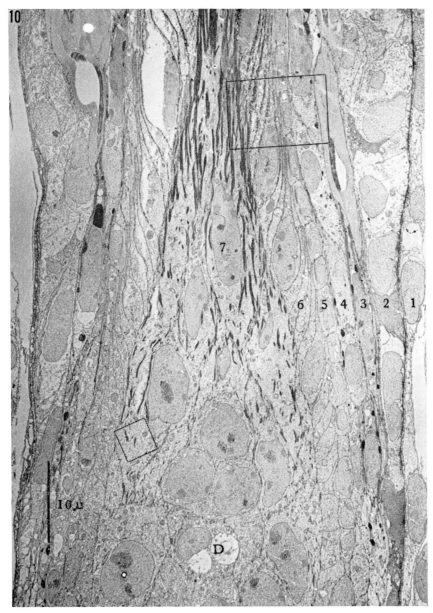

Fig. 10. Longitudinal section through an active hair follicle of the adult white mouse. The section is parasagittal and only a small fraction of the dermal papilla (D) is seen. The cell layers can be identified as follows: (1) connective tissue, (2) outer root sheath, (3) Henle's layer, (4) Huxley's layer, (5) cuticle of inner root sheath, (6) hair cuticle, (7) hair cortex. (×2250).

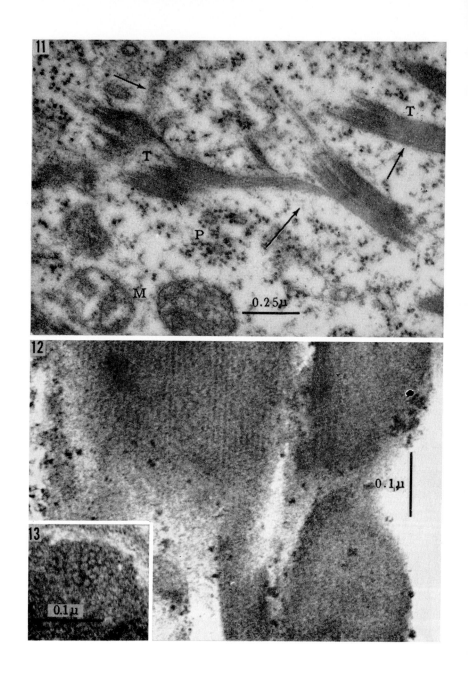

Hard Keratin

Hair and Claw

The formation of hard keratin in the hair is studied to best advantage in longitudinal sections (Fig. 10). The labeling in this figure is similar to that employed in the cross section (Fig. 7) and need not be repeated here. It is relatively easy to follow the various layers downward toward the bulb of the follicle. Note in particular the scalelike arrangement of the cells of the cuticle of the cortex. The dark opaque material within the cuticle cells becomes conspicuous in the upper third of the figure. The cortex of the hair can be identified by the long tonofibrils. These appear spherical in cross sections.

The most conspicuous difference between the formation of hard and soft keratin is the *absence of trichohyalin granules* in the production of hard keratin. This is evident not only in the hair cortex but also in the claw of one-day-old rats (Fig. 15). This difference is especially conspicuous when the claw is compared with the skin of the same animal in which the keratohyalin granules stand out (Fig. 15). In both the hair cortex and the claw, the low-magnification view shows tonofibrils oriented in the direction of growth (Figs. 10, 15). A sharp demarcation exists between the cortex and the cuticle of the hair as also one exists between the keratogenous layer of the claw and the sterile bed. A high-magnification view of the keratogenous zone of the claw (Fig. 16) or hair cortex (Fig. 11) yields the same picture. In both cases there are scattered mitochondria, but more conspicuous is the presence of submicro-

Fig. 11. Detail of the hair cortex of the adult mouse, enlarged from an area similar to the one indicated by a small box in Fig. 10. The first appearance of tonofilaments (T) is characterized by dense interfilamentous substance and peripheral "wisps" of material (arrows). Abundant RNP particles (P) and some mitochondria (M) are present (×61,400).

Fig. 12. Longitudinally sectioned tonofilaments of adult mouse hair cortex. The filaments are arranged parallel to each other and embedded in a dense matrix (×172,000).

Fig. 13. Detail of cross-sectioned tonofilaments of adult mouse hair cortex showing circular profiles (×194,000).

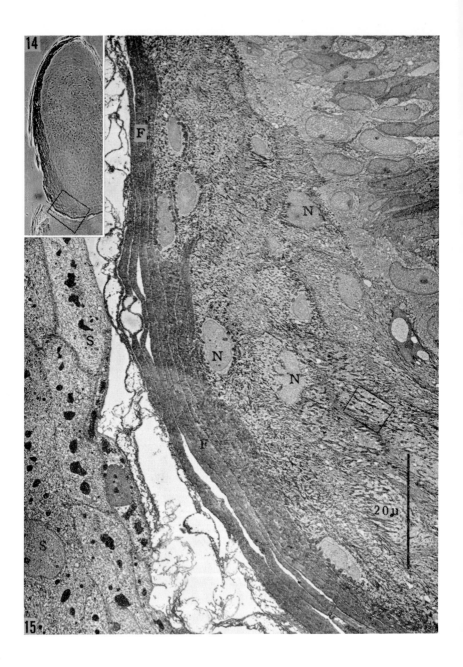

scopic ribonucleoprotein (RNP) particles and tonofilaments. In addition, another cytoplasmic component appears to be involved in the process of hard keratin formation. This is an irregular wisplike material seen in the vicinity of RNP particles and on the lateral sides of aggregations of tonofilaments (Fig. 11).

Fewer free irregular tonofilaments are seen than is the case in soft keratin. In the hair cortex and claw, the tonofilaments are more regular and more parallel for greater lengths. The tonofilaments appear to be embedded in a rather dense material, and there is less evidence of tubule formation although there is evidence of tubules in the final product (Fig. 13).

AMORPHOUS KERATIN

Hair Cuticle

A type of material develops in the cuticle of the hair which is unlike the keratin in the cortex and the inner root sheath of the hair. It appears at almost the same level as the keratogenous zone of the hair cortex (Fig. 10). Because of the scalelike appearance of the cuticle cells this material also first appears in a scalelike pattern increasing in density toward the free end of the hair (Fig. 21). When the cell in which this structure appears is examined at high magnification, one sees in addition to the usual cytoplasmic organelles an irregular extremely dense amorphous substance (Fig. 22). In sections, their profiles may appear spherical, angular, as irregularly short beaded rods and, in general, pleomorphic. They are not surrounded by a membrane. Where they first appear one sees some profiles which are less dense than others, or in some cases the profiles may have less dense areas. As with other cells which undergo keratinization, the cytoplasmic constituents which appear to

---

Fig. 14. Phase contrast micrograph of a longitudinally sectioned claw of one-day-old rat. Plastic section, unstained (×260).

Fig. 15. Low-magnification electron micrograph of an area similar to the box in Fig. 14. The nonkeratinized cells (N) of the claw bed contain numerous tonofibers but no keratohyalin granules. In contrast, the cells (S) of the adjoining fold of skin contain keratohyalin granules which are quite prominent and occur in great abundance. The claw is formed by fully keratinized cells (F) which consist of hard keratin (×1500).

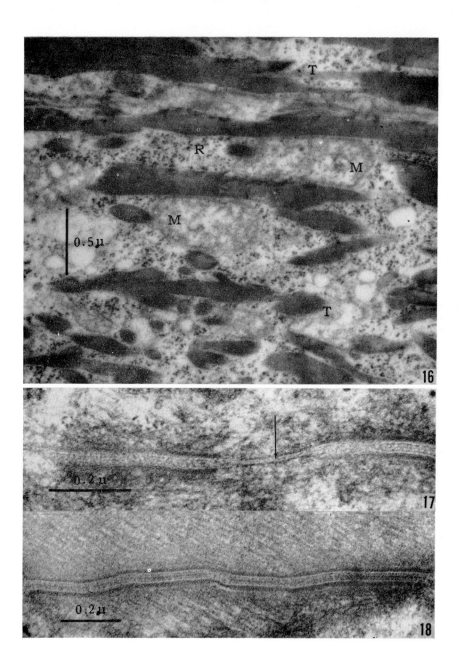

be most closely associated with their formation are free RNP particles. These particles are extremely numerous in the vicinity of the forming amorphous keratin. In cells somewhat higher up, the dense profiles grow by fusion with neighboring profiles and possibly lateral growth may also occur. In the latter stages of this fusion, the cytoplasmic organelles, such as RNP particles and mitochondria, appear to be trapped in the fusion process. Just before the final fusion which results in mature cuticle, extremely dense irregular bodies of small size (Fig. 23) are seen between the relatively large masses of fusing amorphous keratin.

THE FINAL STRUCTURE OF SOFT, HARD, AND AMORPHOUS KERATIN

Soft Keratin

When soft keratin is examined with relatively high magnification, it seems to consist of cells which are dominated by tonofilaments (Fig. 6). Occasional remnants of cell organelles such as mitochondria are seen. The tonofilaments are so organized as to suggest that they form a tubular structure. Many profiles of two parallel filaments can be seen. In sections they appear to travel for short distances in directions distinctly different from other parallel filaments. There are also to be seen, numerous circular profiles and occasional oval profiles. Irregular profiles are also seen. The cell membranes of these cells are rather dense and broad when compared with the cell membranes of underlying nonkeratinized cells. They measure 100 A in width. Between the cells is an amorphous material which appears to split when the cells are mechanically separated. In other places where the cells are slightly removed from each other, thin

---

Fig. 16.   Detail of an area similar to the one indicated by the box in Fig. 15. Tonofibrils (T) are longitudinally cross-sectioned. The cytoplasm contains numerous small RNP particles (R) and some mitochondria (M) but no keratohyalin granules (×35,000).

Fig. 17.   Two desmosomes in the esophagus of the adult mouse. Note that there is an intercellular dense layer (arrow) not related to desmosomes (×114,000).

Fig. 18.   Detail of the contact area between two fully keratinized Henle's cells of the adult mouse hair follicle (×79,000).

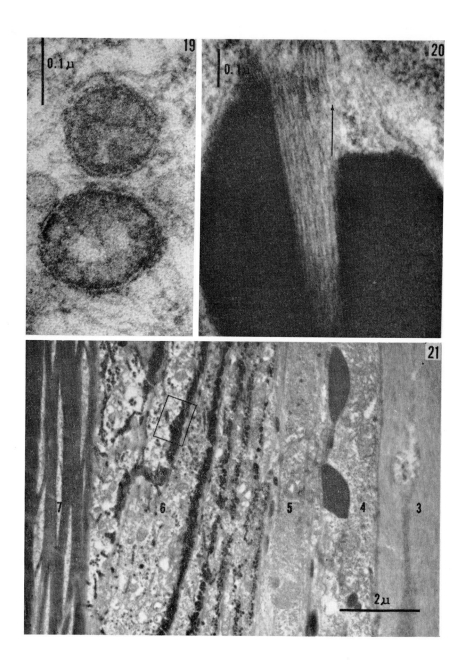

amorphous material is irregularly dispersed. Occasionally, one observes isolated rectangles of a more dense substance between two cells, presumably corresponding to intercellular desmosomal material. One can see a slight thickening of the cell membranes of two adjacent cells in relation to this rectangular substance. However, this thickening of the cell membrane is not always to be seen.

Hard Keratin

Hard keratin consists of cells which are tightly packed with mature tonofilaments. These are rigidly organized so that when they are examined with high magnification, they appear as many parallel straight lines (Fig. 12). Between the parallel tonofilaments is a substance of intermediate density. These cells do not reveal a distinct cell membrane as one sees in cells with soft keratin. However, there is between the individual cells a cement substance which has about the same density of the cell itself (Fig. 26). The tubular nature of hard keratin is indicated by regular circular profiles which can be seen when cut in cross sections (Fig. 13).

Amorphous Keratin

Amorphous keratin consists of dense material in which no filamentous structures have been observed (Fig. 24). The cell outlines are distinct with a narrow layer of cement material between the cells (Fig. 26). In the younger cuticle cells there appears a narrow band of more dense substance on the surface side of the cell. This band increases in thickness in older cells so that it may occupy as much

---

Fig. 19.   Adult mouse esophagus. Two spherical bodies with an average diameter of 0.15 micron. They are of unknown origin and function but have been observed in tongue, skin, and esophagus (×175,000).

Fig. 20.   Adult mouse hair. This indicates the close topographic relation between the trichohyalin granule and the tonofilaments as seen in the early stages of keratinization in the Huxley's layer. The individual tonofilaments tend to run parallel (arrow) for short distances (×98,000).

Fig. 21.   Detail of an area similar to the larger rectangle indicated in Fig. 10 showing some layers of a longitudinally sectioned mouse hair follicle: (3) keratinized Henle's layer, (4) Huxley's layer with trichohyalin granules, (5) cuticle of inner root sheath, (6) scalelike cells of hair cuticle with dense amorphous granules aggregated at the outer boundaries of the cells, (7) hair cortex with fusing dense tonofibrils of hard keratin (×10,800).

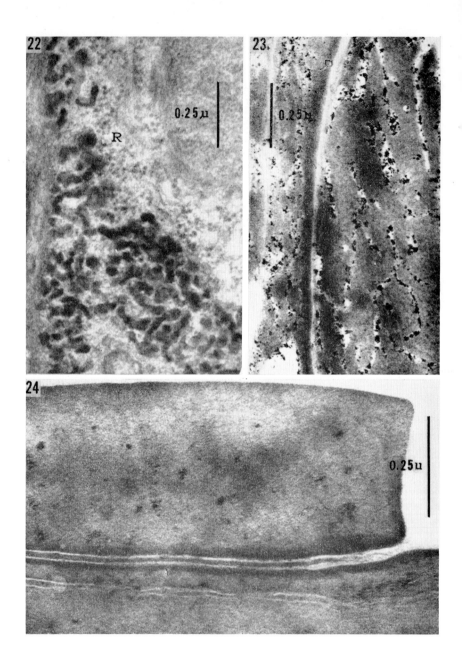

as one-third of the cell width at the outer region of the cell. In addition to this well-organized dense band, there are also present islands of dense material within these cells. Finally, in the mature hair (Figs. 25, 26) there are many bits of extremely dense material of irregular size. Much of this is located between the cells. However, some can be clearly identified as being within the cells.

In comparing the structure of the three types of keratin one notes: Soft keratin consists of irregular arrays of tonofilaments with relatively little dense background. Upon closer examinations the tonofilaments are seen to be parts of tubules. The hard keratin consists of regular tonofilaments with a large amount of dense interfilamentous material. Again, there is evidence that these filaments are parts of tubules. The amorphous keratin consists of dense material and no filaments.

Discussion

Because of histochemical and staining properties, light microscopists have in the past been reluctant to assign a role to keratohyalin in the formation of keratin. For example, Montagna (1956) states in his monograph on skin: "The lack of either sulfhydryl or disulfide groups in the keratohyalin granules eliminates almost entirely the possibility that they play a primary role in keratinization." Such a position is not supported by our findings. There have also been disagreements among electron microscopists on the role of keratohyalin. For example, Birbeck and Mercer (1957a,b,c), Birbeck *et al.* (1956), and Mercer (1958) maintain that keratohyalin transforms into the 100-A fibrils which they demonstrate make up

---

Fig. 22.   Detail of an area similar to the one indicated by a rectangle in Fig. 21 showing the amorphous dense material of the young hair cuticle cells. RNP particles (R) are also present ($\times 68,400$).

Fig. 23.   Similar area as seen in Fig. 22 but more distally located where the hair cuticle has become more solidified and the amorphous material has grown and fused. The fine, extremely electron dense particles are of unknown nature ($\times 68,400$).

Fig. 24.   Detail of the edge of a mature cuticle cell of the adult mouse hair. The amorphous dense profiles have disappeared and are now transformed into a solid, structureless mass. Hair cortex is at the bottom of the figure ($\times 109,000$).

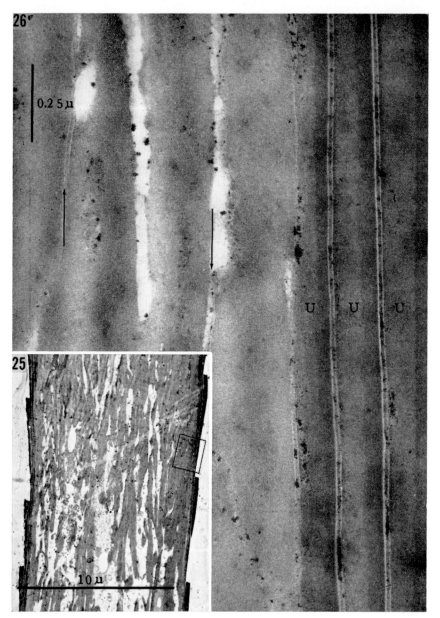

Fig. 25. Low-magnification electron micrograph of the mature hair in the adult white mouse with imbricated cuticular cells (×4300).

Fig. 26. Detail of an area similar to the one indicated in Fig. 25. The three cuticle cells (U) show dense intercellular band which is less obvious between the keratinized cells of the hair cortex (arrows) (×83,000).

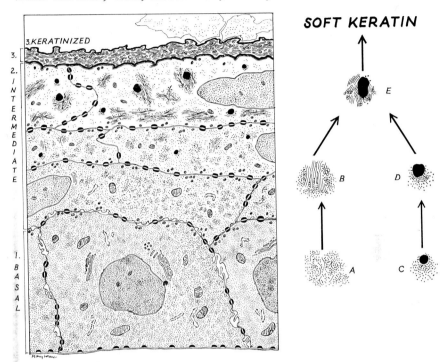

SOFT KERATIN

Fig. 27.   Schematic representation of the changes associated with the formation of *soft keratin* as studied in the tongue and skin of newborn rats and in
the esophagus of adult mice. On the left is a diagram of surface epithelium
undergoing soft keratinization. On the right is a scheme which outlines the
sequence of events which occurs during the formation of soft keratin. A. The
first indication is the appearance of delicate tonofilaments closely associated
with RNP particles. B. The tonofilaments grow and aggregate as more filaments are formed. RNP particles are also closely associated with these events.
C. While the aggregation of tonofilaments is in progress, the formation of
keratohyalin granules begins. These are seen as small spherical masses surrounded by RNP particles. D. The spherical keratohyalin granules, surrounded
by RNP particles, continue to increase in size. The larger keratohyalin granules become somewhat irregular in outline. E. The largest tonofilaments become associated with the irregular keratohyalin granules prior to the final
stabilization and consolidation which results in soft keratin. The keratinized
cell has a broad cell membrane.

keratin. This view is also not supported by our findings. Brody
(1959a,b), on the other hand, maintains in an early paper that
tonofilaments and keratohyalin associate just prior to keratin formation which is more in agreement with our position; however, in a

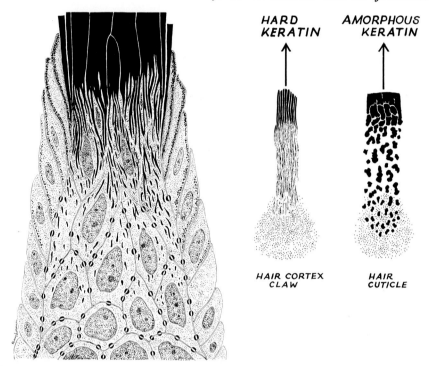

Fig. 28.　Schematic representation of the changes associated with the formation of hard and amorphous keratin as studied in the cuticle and cortex of adult mouse hair follicles. On the left is a diagram of a parasagittal section of a growing hair follicle. Cells of the cuticle are on both sides, showing the imbricated arrangement. The inner cells are part of the hair cortex. On the right are two schematic outlines illustrating the sequence of events which occur during the formation of hard and amorphous keratin. *Hard keratin:* The first sign in the formation of hard keratin is the appearance of tonofilaments closely associated with RNP particles. Continued formation of tonofilaments occurs along with stabilizing material. The filaments then aggregate and coalesce to form hard keratin. *Amorphous keratin:* Amorphous keratin is first recognized as irregular, dense homogeneous bodies surrounded by RNP particles. These grow in width, length, and lateral fusion to form amorphous keratin.

later paper (Brody, 1960) he denies the existence of keratohyalin granules.

On the basis of our observations, we postulate that the steps in the formation of *soft keratin* (Fig. 27) are as follows.

The first step detectable with the electron microscope is the appearance of small delicate filaments, 35-A units in width. The most conspicuous cell structures present during this time are free RNP particles. Golgi apparatus and endoplasmic reticulum are present in certain simple systems, but they may not be basic to the process. The filaments increase in thickness to about 60-A units with free RNP particles still the most likely participant in their formation. They then aggregate and coalesce to form the fibrils which are visible with the light microscope. During the growth and aggregation of tonofilaments, keratohyalin granules appear, surrounded by free RNP particles. These also grow with continued participation of RNP. Finally, the aggregated tonofilaments and keratohyalin granules associate as one of the last steps in the formation of soft keratin. The final stabilization and consolidation occur after the cell boundaries have increased in thickness and become denser.

The first step in the formation of *hard keratin* (Fig. 28) is the production of tonofilaments through the activity of RNP particles. The second step consists of the simultaneous production of additional tonofilaments and stabilizing dense material. The third step entails the growth of these filaments in length and by lateral fusion to form the fibrils which are visible with the light microscope. This growth continues until hard keratin is complete.

The steps in the formation of the *amorphous keratin* of the hair cuticle (Fig. 28) are the formation of irregular dense homogeneous bodies which grow in width, length, and by lateral fusion. Free RNP particles are again the most likely participant in their formation. The continued formation and subsequent growth and fusion result in mature cuticular material.

As a general statement regarding keratinization, it can be said that in all cases, cytoplasmic remnants may be trapped and obscured between the condensing keratinous material. In mature hard keratin, one can see the strict parallel arrangements of filaments. In mature soft keratin, the filaments are less regularly arranged. In amorphous keratin, no filaments are observable in our preparations.

There is no doubt that keratinization is a many-sided process. There is also no doubt that in the development of hard and soft keratin there are similarities and there are differences. If one were to look at just one structural feature of keratinization such as the sulfur-containing amino acids and to compare their distribution and localization during the development of hard and soft keratin, one might readily conclude that there are no differences between hard and soft keratin (Barrnett, 1953; Barrnett and Seligman, 1952). Or if morphological observations were confined to examination of tonofilaments, one might assume that there are no differences between hard and soft keratin. Whereas there are, undoubtedly, similarities, there are also differences, and it is on the basis of the differences that we employ the designation of hard and soft keratin. In this position we agree with the stand of Leblond (1951) that a separation of keratin into different types is valid.

The most conspicuous difference between the formation of hard and soft keratin is the presence of keratohyalin granules in the development of soft keratin and their absence in the development of hard keratin. We feel that the most likely function of the keratohyalin granule is to provide for the stabilization of tonofilaments since after their association with keratohyalin granules, the tonofilaments are more consolidated than they are in deeper layers. Indeed, the thin profile of the keratinized cell indicates that some consolidation does occur. A similar conspicuous structure in the stabilization of tonofilaments is not observed in the formation of hard keratin. It may well be that the stabilizing substance for the tonofilaments in hard keratin is produced simultaneously along with the tonofilaments. Indeed, a fine irregular material is seen (Fig. 11) which might be related to this function. A striking observation has been that free RNP particles are closely associated with the keratinization process. For example, they are the only structures which are intimately related to the keratohyalin granules during their early state of existence. Free RNP particles are the only conspicuous organelles in the general vicinity of the developing tonofilaments in soft keratin. Again, they are conspicuously present in the development of hard keratin and of amorphous keratin.

Some doubt has been expressed by Brody (1960) as to the identity of these particles on the basis of their shape being different from the shape of RNP particles of pancreas. We also have noted a difference in shape in the RNP particles seen in keratinizing epithelium as compared to gland epithelium. However, since RNP particles contain not only RNA but also material related to the synthesis of special products, we rather expect that the RNP particles related to synthesis in pancreas would show some difference from the RNP particles related to synthesis in keratinizing epithelium. Moreover, histochemical studies (Montagna, 1956) demonstrate clearly the presence of RNA in keratinizing epithelium and the presence of a ring of RNA around the keratohyalin granules. This distribution of RNA around keratohyalin granules as observed with histochemical methods conforms to the distribution of RNP particles as seen with the electron microscope.

It should be borne in mind that the schemes of keratinization which we propose above (Figs. 27, 28) were based on observations made with the electron microscope. We realize that the picture thus presented is not complete but must ultimately be correlated with chemical information in order more completely to represent the mechanisms involved.

Acknowledgment. We are indebted to Miss Mary Lorenc for preparing the schematic drawings. We also gratefully acknowledge the skillful assistance of Miss Inger Alexandersson and Miss Marsha Rankin, and the typing of the manuscript by our secretary Mrs. Helen Stark.

REFERENCES

Albright, J. T. 1960. Electron microscope studies of keratinization as observed in gingiva and cheek mucosa. *Ann. N.Y. Acad. Sci.,* 85: 351–361.

Barnicot, N. A., and Birbeck, M. S. C. 1958. The electron microscopy of human melanocytes and melanin granules. *The Biology of Hair Growth,* W. Montagna and R. A. Ellis, Editors. Academic Press, New York. Pp. 239–253.

Barrnett, R. J. 1953. The histochemical distribution of protein-bound sulfhydryl groups. *J. Natl. Cancer Inst.,* 13: 905–925.

Barrnett, R. J., and Seligman, A. M. 1952. Histochemical demonstration of protein-bound sulfhydryl groups. *Science,* 116: 323–327.

Birbeck, M. S. C., and Mercer, E. H. 1957a. The electron microscopy of the human hair follicle. I. Introduction and the hair cortex. *J. Biophys. Biochem. Cytol.,* 3: 203–214.

Birbeck, M. S. C., and Mercer, E. H. 1957b. The electron miscroscopy of the human hair follicle. II. The hair cuticle. *J. Biophys. Biochem. Cytol.,* 3: 215–222.

Birbeck, M. S. C., and Mercer, E. H. 1957c. The electron microscopy of the human hair follicle. III. The inner root sheath and trichohyalin. *J. Biophys. Biochem. Cytol.*, 3: 223–230.

Birbeck, M. S. C., Mercer, E. H., and Barnicot, N. A. 1956. The structure and formation of pigment granules in human hair. *Exptl. Cell Research 10*: 505–514.

Brody, I. 1959a. The keratinization of epidermal cells of normal guinea pig skin as revealed by electron microscopy. *J. Ultrastructure Research, 2*: 482–511.

Brody, I. 1959b. An ultrastructural study on the role of the keratohyalin granules in the keratinization process. *J. Ultrastructure Research, 3*: 84–104.

Brody, I. 1960. The ultrastructure of the tonofibrils in keratinizing process of normal human epidermis. *J. Ultrastructure Research, 4*: 264–297.

Burgos, M. H., and Wislocki, G. B. 1958. The cyclic changes in the mucosa of the guinea pig's uterus, cervix and vagina and in the sexual skin, investigated by the electron microscope. *Endocrinology, 63*: 106–121.

Charles, A., and Smiddy, F. G. 1957. The tonofibrils of the human epidermis. *J. Invest. Dermatol., 29*: 327–338.

Clark, W. H., and Hibbs, R. G. 1958. Electron microscope studies of the human epidermis. The clear cell of Masson (dendritic cell or melanocyte). *J. Biophys. Biochem. Cytol., 4*: 679–684.

Drochmans, P. 1960. Electron microscope studies of epidermal melanocytes, and the fine structure of melanin granules. *J. Biophys. Biochem. Cytol., 8*: 165–180.

Fasske, E., and Themann, H. 1959. Über das Deckepithel der menschlichen Mundschleimhaut. Licht- und elektronenmikroskopische Untersuchungen. *Z. Zellforsch. u. mikroskop. Anat., 49*: 447–463.

Giroud, A., Bulliard, H., and Leblond, C. P. 1934. Les deux types fondamentaux de keratinisation. *Bull. histol. appl. physiol. et pathol. tech. microscop., 11*: 129–144.

Giroud, A., and Leblond, C. P. 1951. The keratinization of epidermis and its derivatives, especially the hair, as shown by x-ray diffraction and histochemical studies. *Ann. N.Y. Acad. Sci., 53*: 613–626.

Gray, M., Blank, H., and Rake, G. 1952. Electron microscopy of normal human skin. *J. Invest. Dermatol., 19*: 449–457.

Hibbs, R. G., and Clark, W. H. 1959. Electron microscope studies of the human epidermis: The cell boundaries and topography of the stratum Malpighii. *J. Biophys. Biochem. Cytol., 6*: 71–76.

Horstmann, E., and Knoop, A. 1958. Elektronmikroskopische Studien an der Epidermis. I. Rattenpfote. *Z. Zellforsch. u. mikroskop. Anat., 47*: 348–362.

Leblond, C. P. 1951. Histological structure of hair, with a brief comparison to other epidermal appendages and epidermis itself. *Ann. N.Y. Acad. Sci., 53*: 464–475.

Matoltsy, A. G., and Balsamo, C. A. 1955. A study of the components of the cornified epithelium of human skin. *J. Biophys. Biochem. Cytol.*, 1: 339–360.

Menefee, M. G. 1957. Some fine structure changes occurring in the epidermis of embryo mice during differentiation. *J. Ultrastructure Research*, 1: 49–61.

Mercer, E. H. 1958. The electron microscopy of keratinized tissues. *The Biology of Hair Growth*, W. Montagna and R. A. Ellis, Editors. Academic Press, New York. Pp. 91–111.

Montagna, W. 1956. *The Structure and Function of Skin*. Academic Press, New York.

Newman, S. B., Borysko, E., and Swerdlow, M. 1949. Ultra-microtomy by a new method. *J. Research Natl. Bur. Standards*, 43: 183.

Odland, G. F. 1958. The fine structure of the interrelationship of cells in the human epidermis. *J. Biophys. Biochem. Cytol.*, 4: 529–538.

Odland, G. F. 1960. A submicroscopic granular component in human epidermis. *J. Invest. Dermatol.*, 34: 11–15.

Ottoson, D., Sjöstrand, F., Stenström, S., and Svaetichin, G. 1953. Microelectrode studies on the E.M.F. of the frog skin related to electron microscopy of the dermo-epidermal junction. *Acta Physiol. Scand.*, 29, suppl. 106: 611–624.

Palade, G. E. 1952. A study of fixation for electron microscopy. *J. Exptl. Med.*, 95: 285.

Pease, D. C. 1951. Electron microscopy of human skin. *Am. J. Anat.*, 89: 469–497.

Pease, D. C. 1952. The electron microscopy of human skin. *Anat. Record*, 112: 373–374.

Pillai, P. A., Guenin, H. A., and Gautier, A. 1960. Les liaisons cellulaires dans l'épiderme du Triton normal au microscope électronique. *Bull. soc. vaudoise. sci. nat.*, 67: 215–221.

Porter, K. R. 1954. Observations on the submicroscopic structure of animal epidermis. *Anat. Record*, 118: 433.

Porter, K. R. 1956. Observations on the fine structure of animal epidermis. *Proc. Third Intern. Conference on Electron Microscopy*, R. Ross, Editor Royal Microscopical Society, London, Pp. 539–546.

Rhodin, J. 1954. Correlation of ultrastructural organization and function in normal and experimentally changed proximal convoluted tubule cells of the mouse kidney. Thesis. Karolinska Institutet, Stockholm.

Rogers, G. E. 1959. Electron microscopy of wool. *J. Ultrastructure Research*, 2: 309–330.

Selby, C. C. 1955. An electron microscopic study of the epidermis of mammalian skin in thin sections. I. Dermo-epidermal junction and basal cell layer. *J. Biophys. Biochem. Cytol.*, 1: 425–444.

Selby, C. C. 1956. The fine structure of human epidermis as revealed by the electron microscope. *J. Soc. Cosmetic Chemists*, 7: 584–599.

Selby, C. C. 1957. An electron microscope study of thin sections of human skin. II. Superficial cell layers of foot pad epidermis. *J. Invest. Dermatol.*, 29: 131–150.

Setälä, K., Merenmies, L., Stjernvall, L., Nyholm, M. 1960a. Mechanism of experimental tumorigenesis. IV. Ultrastructure of interfollicular epidermis of nomal adult mouse. *J. Natl. Cancer Inst.*, 24: 329–353.

Setälä, K., Merenmies, L., Stjernvall, L., Nyholm, M., and Aho, Y. 1960b. Mechanism of experimental tumorigenesis. V. Ultrastructural alterations in mouse epidermis caused by span 60 and tween 60-type agents. *J. Natl. Cancer Inst.*, 24: 355–385.

Sjöstrand, F. S. 1953. The ultrastructure of the outer segments of rods and cones of the eye as revealed by the electron microscope. *J. Cellular Comp. Physiol.*, 42: 15.

Sognnaes, R. F., and Albright, J. T. 1956. Preliminary observations on the fine structure of oral mucosa. *Anat. Record, 126*: 225–240.

Sognnaes, R. F., and Albright, J. T. 1958. Electron microscopy of the epithelial lining of the human oral mucosa. *Oral Surg. Oral Med. Oral Pathol., 11*: 662.

Themann, H. 1958. Elektronenmikroskopische Untersuchungen der normalen und der pathologisch veränderten Mundschleimhaut. *Fortschr. Kiefer- u. Gesichtschir., 4*: 390–398.

Vogel, A. 1958. Zelloberfläche und Zellverbindung im elektronenmikroskopischen Bild. *Verhandl. deut. Ges. Pathol.*, 284–295.

Weiss, P., and Ferris, W. 1954. Electronmicrograms of larval amphibian epidermis. *Exptl. Cell Research, 6*: 546–549.

5

Influence of Vitamin A on Keratinization*

Howard A. Bern and Donald J. Lawrence †
Department of Zoology and Its Cancer Research Genetics Laboratory, University of California, Berkeley

For many years a relationship between vitamin A and keratinization has been recognized (Mori, 1922; Evans and Bishop, 1922), but the nature of the influence of the vitamin on epithelia has not been well understood. However, new experimental findings are helping to clarify our view of the relationship; consequently, the present survey is focused on recent developments.

In conditions in which there is a *deficiency of vitamin A*, keratinization is somehow favored: many or all external areas of the mammal appear to be more heavily keratinized than normally, and most ectoderm-derived glands and "mucous membranes," as well as at least some epithelia of endodermal origin, appear to undergo keratinization (Wolbach and Bessey, 1942; Moore, 1957). The latter process of ectopic keratinization appears likely to be one of a local metaplastic alteration of the epithelium, although there is little experimental evidence to rule out other possible mechanisms, such as an ingrowth of normally keratinizing epithelium in areas adjacent to the orifices. The effects of vitamin A deficiency are discussed elsewhere in this symposium by Parnell and Sherman.

The converse of the vitamin A-epithelium relation, the effects on normal keratinization of an *excess of vitamin A*, has been investigated with less certain conclusions. It has been reasoned that if a

* Supported in part by cancer research funds of the University of California.
† Trainee under U.S. Public Health Service Grant CRT-5045.

lack of the vitamin favors hyperkeratosis and keratinizing meta-plasia, then an excess might inhibit normal keratinization. It is the latter possibility which concerns us here. Domagk and Dobeneck (1933) first described the epithelial changes produced by excess vitamin A. After large oral doses of the vitamin, the normally keratinizing epithelium of the rat forestomach showed a thinning of the stratum corneum and an increase both in total thickness and in number of the subcorneal cell layers. Similar changes in the oral epithelium of monkeys after large oral doses of vitamin A were reported by Ziskin et al. (1943).

Studer and Frey (1949) observed the effects of excess vitamin A on the epidermis. Large oral doses of the vitamin were administered to rats; after 3 days of such treatment, epidermal thickening, to-gether with swelling and vacuolization of the Malpighian (supra-basal) cells, was observed. Proliferation did not appear to be prominent at this stage, although the mitotic index was not re-ported. Later, after 4 to 12 days of treatment, the epidermis became even thicker and showed a well-defined stratum granulosum as well as evidence of basal-cell proliferation. The authors pointed out a fact applicable to all conventional histologic studies of keratiniz-ing epithelia: little can be said with assurance of the state of the stratum corneum, since the histologic technic employed often re-sults in splitting off and partial loss of the more superficial layers. After several days of continued vitamin A treatment, epidermal al-terations were reduced in degree, and finally disappeared altogether, to result in a normal-appearing epidermis. In a later paper, Studer and Frey (1952) reported a significant 33% increase in epidermal thickness after 4 days of vitamin A treatment; this thickening was accompanied by a 50% increase in colchicine-arrested mitoses. The epidermal thickening and hyperplasia produced by vitamin A were reduced strikingly by injections of cortisone.

The vaginal epithelium of the ovariectomized rat treated with estrogen undergoes a continuous typical keratinization with the production of a prominent stratum granulosum and a definite stratum corneum. Kahn and Bern (1950) found that application of large amounts of vitamin A locally to the keratinizing vagina dra-matically modified the superficial layer of the vaginal mucosa (Figs.

1–4) from one composed of keratinized, anucleate plaques to one composed of spheroidal, nucleated cells. The appearance of the altered cells suggested possible early mucification. Similar findings were reported also by Hohlweg (1951, 1952). In later studies by Kahn (1954a), even as little as 1 unit of vitamin A per day applied locally to the vaginal epithelium was found to have an antikeratinizing effect. Still later, Kahn (1954b, 1959) found that organ cultures of prepuberal rat vagina, exposed to vitamin A *in vitro,* showed inhibited (but not completely suppressed) keratinization. Lasnitzki (personal communication) now has established conclusively the *in vitro* inhibition of vaginal keratinization by vitamin A.

Local application of vitamin A to the skin of the rat (Sabella *et al.,* 1951; Bern *et al.,* 1955a), mouse (Lawrence and Bern, 1958), guinea pig (Montagna, 1954; Bern *et al.,* 1955a), and young chicken (Lawrence and Bern, unpublished) produces an epidermal thickening, with increased prominence of the stratum granulosum, after several days of treatment (Figs. 5–12). These changes are identical with those described earlier by Studer and Frey (1949) in the rat after oral administration for 4 to 12 days of massive amounts of vitamin A. However, the local application of the vitamin produces only local epidermal hypertrophy, with no changes evident in the skin at distant sites. Furthermore, no "adaptation" of the epidermis was observed even after local treatment for as long as 90 days (Bern *et al.,* 1955a).

Some criticism can be directed at earlier studies involving topical application, because (*a*) only massive amounts of the vitamin were employed; (*b*) the oily vehicles alone produced various degrees of epidermal damage, including thickening; (*c*) no control was provided for the influence of the hair cycle, which is known to influence not only epidermal thickness (Chase *et al.,* 1953) but also the degree and type of response of the epidermis to various chemical and physical agents (Chase and Montagna, 1951; Argyris, 1954; Argyris and Bell, 1959). In studies of the effect of local applications of vitamin A to mouse skin, Lawrence and Bern (1958) found that when a minimally "irritating" vehicle was employed, the following points became clear: (*a*) epidermal thickening as well as increase in mitotic index was roughly proportional to the amount of vitamin

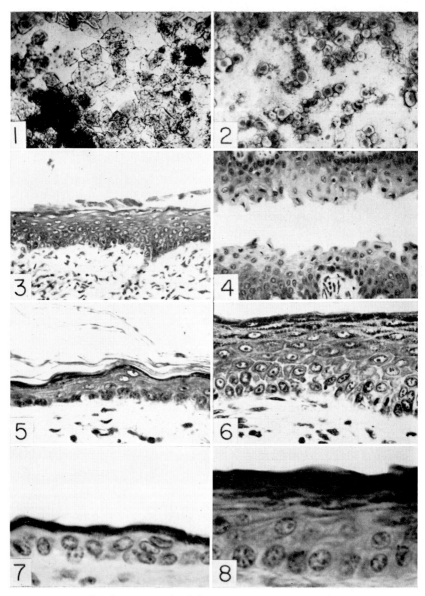

Figs. 1–8. The figures on the left represent various epithelia treated with control substances. The figures on the right represent corresponding epithelia after treatment with vitamin A.

A applied, and was seen even after small amounts of the vitamin (1 unit per day); (b) oleic acid, an effective "irritant" of rodent epidermis, produced no effect even at levels 300 times that of the minimally effective dose level of vitamin A employed; (c) the epidermal response to vitamin A at low dose levels was influenced only minimally by the stage of the hair cycle. These observations suggest a more-or-less "specific" hyperplastic effect of the vitamin upon rodent epidermis, but it was nevertheless not possible to establish any real effect of the vitamin on keratinization. In contrast to others (Setälä, 1960; Setälä et al., 1960), we do not feel that epidermal thickening is proof of an altered differentiation rate. The increase in thickness could be accounted for solely by increased mitoses.

Local epidermal thickening with increased prominence of the

Fig. 1.   Vaginal smear from ovariectomized, estrogen-treated rat after 6 daily topical applications of sesame oil control vehicle. Note large number of anucleate keratinized placques. Wright's stain, ×67 (Kahn and Bern, 1950; reprinted by permission).

Fig. 2.   Vaginal smear from ovariectomized, estrogen-treated rat after 6 daily topical applications of 1500 units vitamin A per day in sesame oil. Note preponderance of nucleated spheroidal epithelial cells; cf. Fig. 1. Wright's stain, ×67 (Kahn and Bern, 1960; reprinted by permission).

Fig. 3.   Vaginal epithelium from ovariectomized, estrogen-treated rat after 6 daily topical applications of sesame oil control vehicle. Note typically keratinized epithelium, presence of stratum granulosum. Hematoxylin-eosin, × approx. 150 (from R. H. Kahn. unpublished).

Fig. 4.   Vaginal epithelium from ovariectomized, estrogen-treated rat after 6 daily topical applications of 1500 units vitamin A per day in sesame oil. Note absence of stratum corneum and stratum granulosum; cf. Fig. 3. Hematoxylin-eosin, × approx. 150 (from R. H. Kahn, unpublished).

Fig. 5.   Rat epidermis after topical treatment with sesame oil control vehicle for 10 days. Hematoxylin-eosin, ×360 (Sabella et al., 1951; reprinted by permission).

Fig. 6.   Rat epidermis after topical treatment with vitamin A (3700 units/day) in sesame oil for 10 days. Note epidermal thickening, prominence of stratum granulosum; cf. Fig. 5. Hematoxylin-eosin, ×360 (Sabella et al., 1951; reprinted by permission).

Fig. 7.   Mouse epidermis after topical treatment with dilute Aquasol control vehicle for 10 days. Hematoxylin-eosin, ×725 (Lawrence and Bern, 1958; reprinted by permission).

Fig. 8.   Mouse epidermis after topical treatment with vitamin A (100 units/day) in dilute Aquasol vehicle for 10 days. Note epidermal thickening, prominence of stratum granulosum; cf. Fig. 7. Hematoxylin-eosin, ×725 (Lawrence and Bern, 1958; reprinted by permission).

stratum granulosum has been reported after local injection of large amounts of vitamin A in the rabbit (Jewell *et al.*, 1957), man (Klauder, 1960), guinea pig and hamster (Gold *et al.*, 1960). However, local intermittent application of vitamin A has been reported to have no effect on the skin of man (Fisher and Herrmann, 1957) nor on the hamster cheek pouch (Gold *et al.*, 1960). In view of the definite effects observed in these same tissues after other means of application of the vitamin (Klauder, 1960; Lawrence *et al.*, 1960), it seems likely that the vehicle and mode of application may be of considerable importance.

The results of Studer and Frey (1952) and of Lawrence and Bern (1958) revealed a significant increase in mitotic index of epidermis under the influence of vitamin A. Furthermore, Sherman (1959) noted an early increase in mitotic index in both normal and A-deficient mouse epidermis, when these tissues are exposed *in vitro* to low levels of vitamin A; higher levels reduce the mitotic activity. The report by Jewell *et al.* (1957), describing epidermal thickening without increase in mitotic activity after a single local injection in the skin of the rabbit, is open to some question since colchicine was not used; the importance of the use of colchicine in mitotic studies of epidermis has been demonstrated by Bullough (1944) and others. Small amounts of vitamin A appear to stimulate cell division in normally keratinizing epidermis both *in vivo* and *in vitro* by a direct effect on the integument, and to a degree roughly proportional to the applied dose. The resulting hyperplasia, probably along with some cell hypertrophy, could account for the overall epidermal thickening (epidermal hypertrophy) observed in many species after repeated local application of the vitamin. When a large increase in mitotic activity is evident, it does not seem necessary to assume any decrease in rate of differentiation to account for epidermal thickening. Nevertheless, such a possible alteration in rate of differentiation may exist, and deserves critical examination, for example, by employing radioisotopes of more-or-less stable chemical constituents of the keratinizing cell (Downes and Lyne, 1959).

In a study of the response of guinea pig nipple epidermis to estrogen and to vitamin A, Bern *et al.* (1955a) observed a nearly uniform response by epidermis from all regions of that area to vitamin A application. Estrogen, however, produced a marked response at the nipple, a reduced response in the areola, and no response in the circumareolar epidermis. With both agents, the response was one of epidermal thickening with increased prominence of the stratum granulosum. Estrogen, however, exhibited a degree of "organ specificity" not apparent with vitamin A. The vitamin apparently has a much more generalized influence on epithelia.

Perhaps the most striking effects of vitamin A have been demonstrated *in vitro* by Fell (Fell and Mellanby, 1953; Fell, 1957). Organ cultures of embryonic chick skin keratinize normally, but precociously, *in vitro;* the addition of high vitamin A to the medium produced a dramatic mucous metaplasia of the normally keratinizing ectoderm. Metaplastic cells are columnar, pseudostratified, and (under certain culture conditions) ciliated, and often contain intracellular periodic acid-Schiff (PAS)-positive, diastase-resistant material interpreted as mucin. After withdrawal of the vitamin A stimulus, the ectoderm reverts to normal keratinization: no new mucous cells are produced, and those mucous cells already present first appear to undergo a burst of synthetic activity, then later degenerate.

Organ and cell cultures of the adult skin of man and rat are maintained better in the presence of high vitamin A than in its absence (Szabó, 1959). Although atypical basal cells may appear in the presence of large amounts of the vitamin, no definite mucous metaplasia has yet been observed. Weiss and James (1955) reported that dissociated chick embryo skin, exposed briefly *in vitro* to vitamin A, became reconstituted to form an epithelium no longer completely keratinizing, but with areas of secretory cells similar to those observed by Fell. Such cells seemed to persist after withdrawal of the high vitamin A stimulus, and consequently this process was termed an "induction," in the terms proposed by Weiss (1949).

The hamster cheek pouch is the first adult tissue reported to undergo definite mucous metaplasia *in vivo* in response to vitamin A (Lawrence *et al.*, 1960; Lawrence and Bern, 1960). In the golden

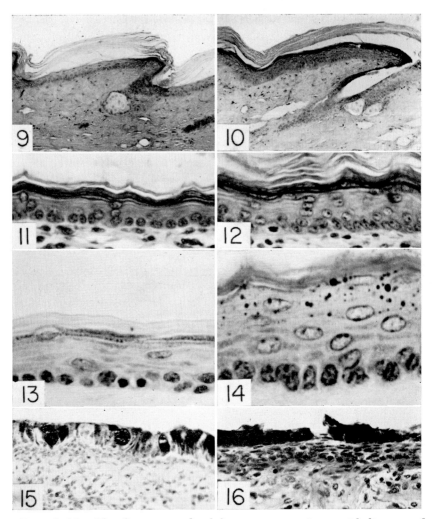

Figs. 9–16. The figures on the left represent various epithelia treated with control substances. The figures on the right represent corresponding epithelia after treatment with vitamin A.

Fig. 9. Mouse tail epidermis after topical application of dilute Aquasol control vehicle for 10 days. Note scales of harder keratin separated by regions of softer keratin. Hematoxylin-eosin, ×100 (Lawrence and Bern, 1958; reprinted by permission).

Fig. 10. Mouse tail epidermis after topical application of vitamin A (100 units/day) in dilute Aquasol vehicle for 10 days. Note lack of harder variety of keratin and continuity of stratum granulosum-containing keratinizing epithelium ("soft"); cf. Fig. 9. Hematoxylin-eosin, ×100 (Lawrence and Bern, 1958; reprinted by permission).

hamster, cheek pouch epithelium bears a strong resemblance to normal interfollicular epidermis, except that it occasionally contains glycogen normally, and has no adnexae such as hair follicles, "rete pegs," or glands. Its lack of adnexae makes it an ideal test organ for studies of keratinization. Vitamin A, when applied in a paraffin pellet maintained in place continuously for several days, produced a variety of changes, depending on the amount of vitamin in the pellet. At lower dose levels, epithelial thickening and increased prominence of the stratum granulosum occurred (Fig. 14), in a manner identical with that previously observed in the epidermis of many species, and in degree roughly proportional to the applied dose level. At these lower dose levels, there were no clear-cut effects upon the stratum corneum except for a proportional increase in thickness. Intermediate dose levels produced a parakeratosis (i.e., stratified polyhedral cells containing nuclear remnants), as well as atypical cells in the lower layers similar to those reported after exposure of epidermis in vitro to high vitamin A (Szabó, 1959); keratohyalin granules also were present. No hyperplastic response was seen in cheek pouches exposed to paraffin pellets without the vitamin (Fig. 13).

Fig. 11. Epidermis from 12-day-old chicken after topical application of dilute Aquasol control vehicle for 10 days. Hematoxylin-eosin, ×525.

Fig. 12. Epidermis from 12-day-old chicken after topical application of vitamin A (100 units/day) in dilute Aquasol vehicle for 10 days. Note epidermal thickening and increased prominence of stratum granulosum; cf. Fig. 11. Hematoxylin-eosin, ×525.

Fig. 13. Epithelium from cheek pouch of golden hamster after treatment for 10 days with control paraffin pellet. Hematoxylin-eosin, ×650 (Lawrence et al., 1960; reprinted by permission).

Fig. 14. Epithelium from cheek pouch of golden hamster after treatment for 10 days with vitamin A (100 units) in paraffin pellet. Note epithelial thickening, prominent keratohyalin granules, stratum corneum; cf. Fig. 13. Hematoxylin-eosin, ×650 (Lawrence et al., 1960; reprinted by permission).

Fig. 15. Mucous metaplasia of hamster cheek pouch epithelium after treatment for 20 days with paraffin pellet containing 50,000 units of vitamin A. Note columnar, mucus-containing epithelial cells on surface of mucosa; cf. Fig. 13. Hematoxylin-eosin, ×185.

Fig. 16. Epithelium of cheek pouch from golden hamster 10 days after cessation of 15-day treatment with vitamin A. Note suggestion of early degenerative changes in overlying mucous cells and of reformation of squamous epithelium beneath mucous cells. Periodic acid-Schiff technic with light hematoxylin stain, ×260.

High dose levels produced a mucous metaplasia (Fig. 15), apparently identical in every respect to that reported earlier *in vitro* by Fell, except that the cheek pouch epithelium exhibited no cilia. In addition, at some higher dose levels, epithelial downgrowths were observed; these were shown to consist of columns of undifferentiated cells (as well as some folds). These downgrowths occasionally included cystic structures. In regions where mucous metaplasia was evident in the surface epithelium, the cysts were lined by mucous cells; where the surface epithelium was parakeratotic, cysts were less frequent and were lined by a parakeratotic epithelium. These mucous cysts and tubular structures were termed "glands" because of their organized appearance; some communicated with the surface epithelium (Lawrence and Bern, 1960).

In another experiment (Lawrence and Bern, unpublished) the occurrence of mucous metaplasia was verified after treatment of cheek pouches for 15 days with vitamin A pellets; the pellets were then removed. After a subsequent 10-day period without treatment, mucous cells were large and swollen, and were frequent in number and widely distributed (Fig. 16). Often they appeared to be degenerating and occasionally were found to overlie regenerating squamous epithelium. These observations, made on a limited number of animals, appear to coincide with the early stages of reversion to a normally keratinizing epithelium observed by Fell *in vitro* after withdrawal of vitamin A.

Electron micrographs of metaplastic areas from the vitamin A-treated hamster cheek pouch (Fig. 17) reveal cells with a large number of complex cytoplasmic organelles, arranged in a manner suggestive of apical polarity, in contrast to the perinuclear arrangement of mitochondria and Golgi membranes in normally keratinizing cheek pouch cells. In addition, metaplastic cells show undifferentiated osmiophilic bodies similar to those reported by Nilsson (1958). Fingerlike microvilli project into the lumen from the free cell surface of the metaplastic cell. The smaller columnar cells shown in Fig. 17 are assumed to represent an early stage in the differentiation of mucous cells, since they are similar in every respect to the early mucous cells reported by Nilsson (1958) in the hormone-stimulated uterine epithelium.

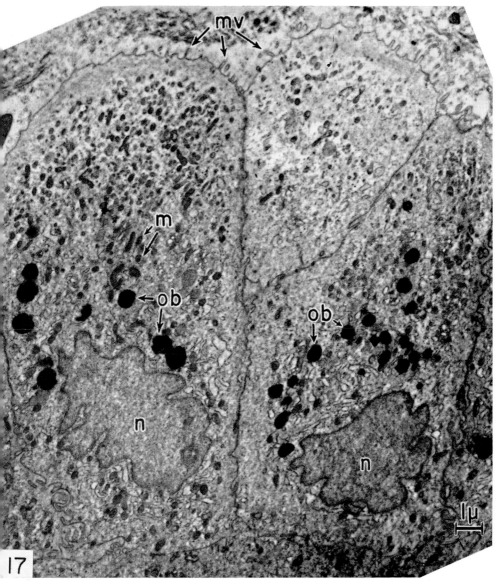

Fig. 17. Electron micrograph of metaplastic hamster cheek pouch lining. Note columnar epithelial cells, polarization of cytoplasmic organelles toward luminal surface. mv, microvilli; ob, osmiophilic bodies; n, nucleus; m, mitochondria. ×6000.

With the production of mucous metaplasia in the adult hamster cheek pouch *in situ* by vitamin A, it now appears certain that the original observations of the vitamin A-produced metaplasia *in vitro* by Fell and by Weiss and James were not indicative of a specialized property of embryonic tissue only nor a consequence of special *in vitro* conditions. Rather, the ability to undergo mucous metaplasia in response to vitamin A appears to be a fundamental property of keratinizing epithelia generally. The two instances of mucous metaplasia observed to date seem unlikely to result from an ingrowth of normal mucous cells from a nearby source; in the *in vitro* systems no such source is known to be present, and in the hamster cheek pouch the nearest source is located at some distance. Furthermore, in the cheek pouch, mucous cells are found in a number of apparently separate metaplastic foci.

The striking alterations in the cell surface structure and in the number and distribution of cytoplasmic organelles seen in electron micrographs of metaplastic epithelium suggest a profound alteration in the synthetic processes of the metaplastic cell compared with the normally keratinizing cell. Several such biochemical alterations have been documented by *in vitro* studies with chick ectoderm by Fell *et al.* (1954) and Pelc and Fell (1960): initially, the rapid uptake of S^{35}-cyst(e)ine seen in normally keratinizing ectoderm is depressed by vitamin A treatment; somewhat later, the uptake of S^{35}-sulfate is increased markedly. Such observations are profoundly significant (Fig. 18) in view of the known importance of cyst(e)ine in normal keratinization (Bern, 1954; Bern *et al.*, 1955b; Harkness and Bern, 1957; Ryder, 1958; Rogers, 1959) and of sulfate in mucus synthesis (cf. Fell *et al.*, 1954).

The mechanism and site of action of vitamin A on epithelia remain unknown. The point of action appears to be within the epithelial tissue, upon the basal epithelial cell; however, an effect could be mediated by immediately adjacent stroma. Tissue culture studies involving epithelial cells without stroma, or studies employing separated and recombined epithelium-stroma combinations (cf. Billingham *et al.*, 1951; Grobstein, 1956; Orr, 1958), may answer this question. The mechanism of action on epithelia, at the biochemical level, may involve some alteration of copper-catalyzed enzymes

(Marston, 1952; Balakhovsky and Drozdova, 1957; Burley *et al.*, 1959), perhaps located in mitochondria (Sheldon and Zetterqvist, 1956), or a relationship to SH-groups and a protein moiety as demonstrated in the retina by Wald and Brown (1952).

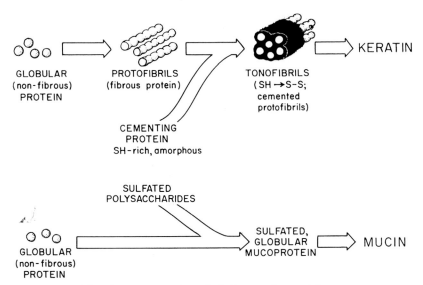

Fig. 18.   Molecular aspects of epithelial metaplasia. Schematic representation of proposed mechanisms of major synthetic patterns in keratinization (above) and mucification (below). Based on the "two-component" hypothesis of keratin formation, as derived in part from the data of Rogers, Birbeck and Mercer, Ryder, Pelc and Fell, Bern and Harkness.

The current body of experimental evidence provides some rationale for the use of vitamin A therapy (Mulay and Urbach, 1958; Zegarelli *et al.*, 1959) in the treatment of leukoplakia, the keratinizing metaplasia of human mucous epithelium. Whether the epithelium of man is capable of expressing its presumed potential of mucous transformation, or even of a real inhibition of keratinization (by becoming parakeratotic), as a response to vitamin A, may depend on the employment of a suitable vehicle and mode of application. Adequate demonstration of any such effect must involve careful control for regional variations in keratinization within the oral cavity (cf. Weinmann and Meyer, 1959), as well as for the effects of the vehicle employed.

At dose levels below those which produce metaplasia, effects on the hamster cheek pouch were observed which are identical with those seen in the epidermis and oral epithelium of several mammalian and avian species. From these observations on the cheek pouch one can postulate a series of responses of keratinizing epithelia to excess vitamin A, depending on the dose level employed. At lower dose levels, hypertrophy is predominant, evidently as a result of increased mitotic rate. At moderate dose levels, parakeratosis is the major response; a marked change in differentiation now predominates over mitotic rate increase. At higher dose levels, mucous metaplasia ensues; accompanying this are changes in growth pattern of the epithelium, producing downgrowths, cysts, and gland-like structures. At still higher dose levels, death of the epithelium (Lawrence *et al.*, 1960) occurs.

Summary

The current body of experimental literature concerning the effects of excess vitamin A on keratinization is reviewed. It is concluded that the effect of excess vitamin A on keratinizing epithelia varies considerably with the dose level applied. At low dose levels, hyperplasia occurs. Intermediate dose levels result in a parakeratosis. High dose levels result in a mucous metaplasia, apparently reversible in time by removing the vitamin A stimulus. Massive dose levels produce death of the epithelium. There is evidence that these responses are generalized and may apply to all keratinizing epithelia.

Acknowledgments. We are indebted to Richard Nishioka for preparation of the electron micrograph reproduced herein and to Victor Duran for the photomicrography.

REFERENCES

Argyris, T. S. 1954. The relationship between the hair growth cycle and the response of mouse skin to x-irradiation. *Am. J. Anat.*, 94: 439–471.

Argyris, T. S., and Bell, E. 1959. The physiologic activity of the skin and its response to ultrasound. *Anat. Record*, 134: 153–169.

Balakhovsky, S. D., and Drozdova, N. N. 1957. A contribution to the study of the mechanism of the action of vitamin A (retinol). The copper-polyene antagonism and keratinization of epithelial tissue. *J. Biochem. U.S.S.R., 22*: 330–335.

Bern, H. A. 1954. Histology and chemistry of keratin formation. *Nature, 174*: 509–511.

Bern, H. A., Alfert, M., and Blair, S. M. 1957. Cytochemical studies of keratin formation and of epithelial metaplasia in the rodent vagina and prostate. *J. Histochem. and Cytochem., 5*: 105–119.

Bern, H. A., Elias, J. J., Pickett, P. B., Powers, T. R., and Harkness, M. N. 1955a. The influence of vitamin A on the epidermis. *Am. J. Anat., 96*: 419–448.

Bern, H. A., Harkness, D. R., and Blair, S. M. 1955b. Radioautographic studies of keratin formation. *Proc. Natl. Acad. Sci. U.S., 41*: 55–60.

Billingham, R. E., Orr, J. W., and Woodhouse, D. L. 1951. Transplantation of skin components during chemical carcinogenesis with 20-methylcholanthrene. *Brit. J. Cancer, 5*: 417–432.

Bullough, H. F. 1944. Cyclical changes in the skin of the mouse during the oestrus cycle. *J. Endocrinol., 3*: 280–287.

Burley, R. W., and Horden, F. W. A. 1959. Experiments on wool from copper-deficient sheep. *Nature, 184*, suppl. 22: 1725–1726.

Chase, H. B., and Montagna, W. 1951. Relation of hair proliferation to damage induced in the mouse skin. *Proc. Soc. Exptl. Biol. Med., 76*: 35–37.

Chase, H. B., Montagna, W., and Malone, J. D. 1953. Changes in the skin in relation to the hair growth cycle. *Anat. Record, 116*: 75–92.

Domagk, G., and von Dobeneck, P. 1933. Ueber histologische Befunde bei der Ueberdosierung mit Vitamin a-Konzentrat. *Arch. pathol. Anat. u. Physiol. Virchow's, 290*: 385–395.

Downes, A. M., and Lyne, A. G. 1959. Measurement of the rate of growth of wool using cystine labelled with sulfur-35. *Nature, 184*: 1834–1837.

Evans, H. M., and Bishop, K. S. 1922. On an invariable and characteristic disturbance of reproductive function in animals reared on a diet poor in fat soluble vitamins A. *Anat. Record, 23*: 17.

Fell, H. B. 1957. The effect of excess vitamin A on cultures of embryonic chicken skin explanted at different stages of differentiation. *Proc. Roy. Soc. (London), B146*: 242–256.

Fell, H. B., and Mellanby, E. 1953. Metaplasia produced in cultures of chick ectoderm by high vitamin A. *J. Physiol. (London), 119*: 470–488.

Fell, H. B., Mellanby, E., and Pelc, S. R. 1954. Influence of excess vitamin A on the sulphate metabolism of chick ectoderm grown *in vitro*. *Brit. Med. J., 2*: 611.

Fisher, L., and Herrmann, F. 1957. Some effects of topical vitamin A upon human epidermis. *Arch. Dermatol., 75*: 667–670.

Gold, L., Morris, A. L., and Seligman, H. G. 1960. Skin and oral mucosal response to single vitamin A injection. *J. Dental Research, 39*: 663.

Grobstein, C. 1956. Inductive tissue interaction in development. *Advances in Cancer Research, 4*: 187–236.

Harkness, D. R., and Bern, H. A. 1957. Radioautographic studies of hair growth in the mouse. *Acta Anat., 31*: 35–45.

Hohlweg, W. 1951. Über die Hemmung der Oestrusreaktion durch Vitamin A-Überdosierung. *Klin. Wochschr., 29*: 193–195.

Hohlweg, W. 1952. Die Testierung von Vitamin A-Präparaten mit Hilfe der Antioestrusreaktion. *Pharmazie, 5*: 280–284.

Jewell, H. A., Taube, H., Nicholls, M. E., and Lehman, R. A. 1957. Action of vitamin A on the skin following intracutaneous injection. *Proc. Soc. Exptl. Biol. Med., 96*: 162–165.

Kahn, R. H. 1954a. Effect of locally applied vitamin A and estrogen on the rat vagina. *Am. J. Anat., 95*: 309–335.

Kahn, R. H. 1954b. Effect of oestrogen and vitamin A on vaginal keratinization in tissue culture. *Nature, 174*: 317.

Kahn, R. H. 1959. Vaginal keratinization *in vitro*. *Ann. N.Y. Acad. Sci., 83*: 347–355.

Kahn, R. H., and Bern, H. A. 1950. Antifolliculoid activity of vitamin A. *Science, 111*: 516–517.

Klauder, J. V. 1960. Treatment of some dermatoses by local injection of vitamin A. *Arch. Dermatol., 81*: 253–259.

Lawrence, D. J., and Bern, H. A. 1958. On the specificity of the response of mouse epidermis to vitamin A. *J. Invest. Dermatol., 31*: 313–325.

Lawrence, D. J., and Bern, H. A. 1960. Mucous metaplasia and mucous gland formation in keratinized adult epithelium *in situ* treated with vitamin A. *Exptl. Cell Research, 21*: 443–446.

Lawrence, D. J., Bern, H. A., and Steadman, M. G. 1960. Vitamin A and keratinization. Studies on the hamster cheekpouch. *Ann. Otol. Rhinol. & Laryngol., 69*: 645–661.

Marston, H. R. 1952. Cobalt, copper, and molybdenum in the nutrition of animals and plants. *Physiol. Revs., 32*: 66–121.

Montagna, W. 1954. Penetration and local effect of vitamin A on the skin of the guinea pig. *Proc. Soc. Exptl. Biol. Med., 86*: 668–672.

Moore, T. 1957. *Vitamin A.* Elsevier, Amsterdam.

Mori, S. 1922. Primary changes in eyes of rats which result from deficiency of fat soluble A in diet. *J. Am. Med. Assoc., 79*: 197–200.

Mulay, D. N., and Urbach, F. 1958. Local therapy of oral leukoplakia with vitamin A. *Arch. Dermatol., 78*: 637–638.

Nilsson, O. 1958. Ultrastructure of mouse uterine surface epithelium under different estrogenic influences. II. Early effect of estrogen administered to spayed rats. *J. Ultrastructure Research, 2*: 73–95.

Orr, J. W. 1958. The mechanism of chemical carcinogenesis. *Brit. Med. Bull.*, *14*: 99–101.

Pelc, S. R., and Fell, H. B. 1960. The effect of excess vitamin A on the uptake of labelled compounds by embryonic skin in organ cultures. *Exptl. Cell Research, 19*: 99–113.

Rogers, G. E. 1959. Electron microscope studies of hair and wool. *Ann. N.Y. Acad. Sci., 83*: 378–399.

Ryder, M. L. 1958. Nutritional factors influencing hair and wool growth. *The Biology of Hair Growth,* W. Montagna and R. A. Ellis, Editors. Academic Press, New York. Pp. 305–335.

Sabella, J. D., Bern, H. A., and Kahn, R. H. 1951. Effect of locally applied vitamin A and estrogen on rat epidermis. *Proc. Soc. Exptl. Biol. Med., 76*: 449–503.

Setälä, K. 1960. Progress in carcinogenesis. Tumor-enhancing factors. A bioassay of skin tumor formation. *Progr. Exptl. Tumor Research, 1*: 225–278.

Setälä, K., Merenmies, L., Stjernvall, L., and Nyholm, M. 1960. Mechanisms of experimental tumorigenesis. IV. Ultrastructure of interfollicular epidermis of normal adult mouse. *J. Natl. Cancer Inst., 24*: 329–354.

Sheldon, H., and Zetterqvist, H. 1956. Experimentally-induced changes in mitochondrial morphology: Vitamin A deficiency. *Exptl. Cell Research, 10*: 225–228.

Sherman, B. S. 1959. The effect of vitamin A on epithelial mitosis *in vitro. Anat. Record, 133*: 429.

Studer, A., and Frey, J. R. 1949. Ueber Hautveränderungen der Ratte nach grossen oralen Dosen von Vitamin A. *Schweiz. med. Wochschr., 79*: 382–384.

Studer, A., and Frey, J. R. 1952. Wirkung von Cortison auf die ruhende und die mit Vitamin A oder Testosteronpropionat zur Proliferation gebrachte Epidermis der Ratte. *Dermatologica, 104*: 1–18.

Szabó, G. 1959. Effect of vitamin A on human skin *in vitro. Excerpta Med. Sect.* I, *13*: 211–212.

Wald, G., and Brown, P. K. 1952. The role of sulfhydryl groups in the bleaching and synthesis of rhodopsin. *J. Gen. Physiol., 35*: 797–821.

Weinmann, J. P., and Meyer, J. 1959. Types of keratinization in the human gingiva. *J. Invest. Dermatol., 32*: 86–94.

Weiss, P. 1949. The problem of cellular differentiation. *Proc. 1st Natl. Cancer Conf.* Pp. 50–60.

Weiss, P., and James, R. 1955. Skin metaplasia *in vitro* induced by brief exposure to vitamin A. *Exptl. Cell Research, suppl. 3*: 381–394.

Wolbach, S. B., and Bessey, O. A. 1942. Tissue changes in vitamin deficiencies. *Physiol. Revs., 22*: 233–289.

Zegarelli, E. V., Kutscher, A. H., and Silvers, H. F. 1959. Keratotic le-
    sions of the oral mucous membranes. Treatment with high dosage
    topical-systematic vitamin A. *N.Y. State Dental J.*, 25: 244–252.
Ziskin, D. E., Rosenstein, S. N., and Drucker, L. 1943. Interrelation of
    large parenteral doses of estrogen and vitamin A and their effect on
    the oral mucosa. *Am. J. Orthodontics Oral Surg.*, 29: 163–177.

6

Effect of Vitamin A on Keratinization in the A-Deficient Rat*

Jerome P. Parnell and Burton S. Sherman
Department of Anatomy, State University of New York, Downstate Medical Center, Brooklyn, New York

Vitamin A is necessary for the maintenance of normal epithelial structures. The vitamin A-deficient state was studied and described quite adequately by Wolbach and Howe (1925). The hyperkeratosis of epithelial tissues after removal of vitamin A from the diet has been studied by Mori (1904), Frazier and Hu (1931), and others.

The results of the topical application of vitamin A to normal epithelial tissues are also well known. Vitamin A, either in oil or aqueous media, produces a general hyperplasia and increase in the thickness of epithelial structures, a specific acanthosis in various layers of the skin and parakeratosis of the stratum corneum. These results are supported by the work of Studer and Frey (1949), Sabella et al. (1951), and Bern et al. (1955).

However, the influence of vitamin A on A-deficient tissues had not been studied until recently. Sobel et al. (1958) established the fact that vitamin A was not only absorbed through the skin but also brought about definite changes at the site of absorption. This work indicated that vitamin A was capable of restoring the A-deficient skin to normal at the site of application.

* This work was supported by the United States Public Health Service, Grant No. RG 4456 (C4).

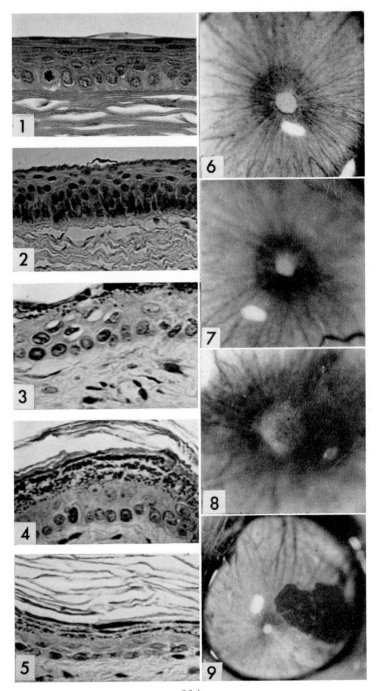

Vitamin A has a definite effect on cytodifferentiation. The work of Fell and Mellanby (1953) shows a distinct change in cellular morphology following the administration of large amounts of vitamin A to tissue culture. Vitamin A is said to have an antikeratinization effect (Harris *et al.*, 1932). Problems concerning the A-deficient state still exist. The relationship of the mitotic rate of tissues to cytodifferentiation and the production of keratin is not well understood.

Further understanding of these problems is sought through the study of the corneal epithelium in the deficient rat and after partial recovery through the introduction of vitamin A locally.

Materials and Methods

The animals used in these experiments were Wistar albino rats of mixed sexes.

At weaning (21–22 days of age), those animals to be rendered vitamin A-deficient were placed on a Vitamin A Test Diet (U.S.P. XIV) and given water ad libitum. The animals were weighed daily throughout the experiment. Animals on the Vitamin A Test Diet were considered depleted when their body weight remained stationary for seven days and/or severe xerophthalmia developed. In addition, some animals exhibited matted and lusterless hair, diarrhea, hunchback posture, and extreme irritability. Normal animals were raised on a stock diet consisting of Big Red Dog Pellets.

The procedure of Bullough was used in studying the effect of vitamin A on the mitotic index of epidermis and corneal and tracheal epithelia *in vitro.** The animals employed in this study consisted

---

* This work was recently published by B. Sherman and is reviewed here. *J. Invest. Dermatol.*, 37: 469–480 (1961).

Fig. 1.   Normal corneal epithelium of rat 42 days of age (×225).
Fig. 2.   Corneal epithelium of rat after 2 weeks on a deficient diet (×225).
Fig. 3.   Corneal epithelium of a rat 4 weeks on the deficient diet. Note intermediate zone.
Fig. 4.   Corneal epithelium of rat showing gross deficiency. Note keratohyalin granules, sloughing keratinized material.
Fig. 5.   Corneal epithelium of rat 6 weeks on a deficient diet.
Figs. 6–9.   Shows advancing signs of deficiency grossly in the eye.

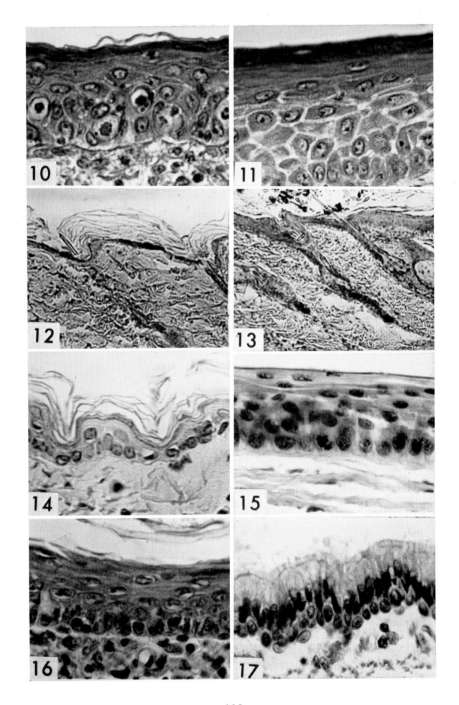

of 21 young male albino rats. Seven animals were placed on the vitamin A-deficient diet, seven were raised on the stock diet, and the remaining seven animals were placed on the A-deficient diet supplemented orally with a daily dose of 30 μg of vitamin A. All animals were sacrificed when physical signs of deficiency were apparent in the first group. Specimens of epidermis, cornea, and trachea were taken from each animal and cut into small pieces (approximately 2 by 4 mm in size). Specimens of tissue of the same type were placed in glass-stoppered flasks containing 4 ml of a phosphate-buffered saline solution at pH 7.4 containing glucose and sodium glutamate (Bullough, 1954; Bullough and Johnson, 1951).

Aqueous suspensions of vitamin A acetate in 16% Tween 20 (a water dispersant) were prepared in concentrations of 10, 100, 1000, and 10,000 μg of vitamin A per milliliter respectively. Tissues were incubated in the buffered solutions containing 1 ml of one of the concentrations of vitamin A. Other specimens of tissues were incubated in buffered solutions containing the aqueous dispersant. Tissues used for controls were incubated in flasks with only the saline-phosphate buffer.

The flasks containing the tissues were placed in a shaking incubator at 38°C and gently rocked for one hour. At this time, 0.016 mg of colchicine dissolved in 0.04 ml of physiologic saline was introduced into each flask. The incubation was continued for 4 hours. The specimens were then fixed in Bouin's solution sectioned in paraffin at 8 microns and stained with Delafield's hematoxylin and eosin. Estimates of mitotic indexes were made by direct counts of

---

Fig. 10. Corneal epithelium of rat in gross deficiency, after the administration of aqueous vehicle, left eye of same animal as shown in Fig. 11.

Fig. 11. Corneal epithelium of rat gross deficiency after treatment with a total of 7 μg of vitamin A, right eye of animal shown in Fig. 10.

Fig. 12. Skin of deficient rat (nontreated site). This animal had been treated locally with vitamin A (see Fig. 13) (×100).

Fig. 13. Skin of deficient rat. This animal was treated locally with vitamin A at this site (×100).

Fig. 14. Grossly deficient corneal epithelium (×150).

Fig. 15. Normal corneal epithelium (×150).

Fig. 16. Tracheal epithelium of grossly deficient rat (×200).

Fig. 17. Normal tracheal epithelium of rat.

1000 consecutive basal cells in the tissues at a magnification of 450×.

For the corneal study, animals were partially anesthetized with Nembutal, and their eyes were examined with the aid of a wide field binocular microscope at a magnification of 40×. The progress of the deficiency was followed daily to the termination of the experiment. Aqueous suspensions of vitamin A* in concentrations of 1, 10, 100, and 1000 μg of vitamin per 0.2 ml were prepared. The preparation was dropped into the conjunctival sac of the right eye of animals. The vehicle consisting of diluted Tween solutions or diluted Aquasol A vehicle was dropped into the left eye. Animals were treated in this manner every 48 hours from seven to fifteen times.

At the termination of the experiment both eyes were removed and fixed in Bouin's fluid for 24 hours. The tissues were then treated routinely and stained with hematoxylin and eosin or Mallory's connective tissue stain.

Observations

The Deficient State

General

The vitamin A-deficient animal is characterized by a definite reduction in the rate of growth and a progressive keratinizing metaplasia of most epithelial structures. The skin, the corneal and tracheal epithelia are all profoundly affected. The skin of the A-deficient animal shows a definite syndrome consisting of cessation of hair growth, thin epidermis, lack of dermal fat, and much thickened stratum corneum (Fig. 12).

If vitamin A is applied locally to an area of the skin many histological changes take place at the site. The epidermis gets thicker and becomes more basophilic. The stratum germinativum and granulosum are increased in size, hair buds begin to grow, and sebaceous glands enlarge. The skin takes on a more normal picture (Fig. 13).

* These solutions were prepared by diluting Aquasol A preparation which was generously donated by the U.S. Vitamin Corp., New York.

The tracheal epithelium of the rat fed the stock diet appears as in Fig. 17. It is pseudostratified ciliated columnar throughout the experimental period. There is an abundance of mucous secreting goblet cells.

The tracheal epithelium of rats on the A-deficient diet remains normal in appearance until approximately the sixth week of the depletion period. At this time, the epithelium is reduced in height and has a decreased number of goblet cells. Squamous metaplasia begins shortly after this period. Areas of squamous cells appear and enlarge by peripheral extension. Usually after the seventh week, the original columnar epithelium is completely replaced by stratified squamous epithelium and now resembles the corneal epithelium (Fig. 16, and compare with Fig. 15).

Cornea

Gross Changes in Eye. As the vitamin A deficiency progresses certain symptoms appear in the eyes of the animals. Gross observations with the naked eye in early stages may reveal little more than a lack of luster. The corners of the eyes may show some irritation, and the vague lusterless conditon so often described may be revealed to be a roughness or sandiness of the surface of the conjunctiva. Close scrutiny of the surface under proper light and magnification reveals an overall graininess which is shown grossly by a slight opacity. These early symptoms can be present in animals that have been denied the vitamin for as little as a week (Fig. 6).

If the regimen is continued this overall opacity increases until the eyes have the so-called dirty window effect shown in Fig. 7. Gross examination reveals a crinkled appearance of the corneal surface which is easily seen with the naked eye. The condition continues in the days that follow and usually becomes more concentrated centrally. A density is now customarily visible either centrally or just to one side of the pupil (Fig. 8). This condition is visible in about 20 to 30 days. The plaque now becomes dense and thickened and completely opaque rendering the animal blind. In the weeks that follow other dense areas may form and thicken only to break up and become dislodged (Fig. 9). The eye fills with a sludge and is partially closed. Subsequent changes are variable as the animal becomes moribund. The eyes may dry, close completely, or become infected. A histological section of a grossly deficient cornea is shown in Fig. 14.

Studies from Eye Washings.   Cells taken from eye washings may reflect significant changes occurring in the corneal epithelium as the deficiency advances. Cells from the normal eye show a moderate number of typical squamous cells. These cells have normal morphological detail. They have an intact deeply staining nucleus and a rather pale granular cytoplasm. There is very little variation in their size and they are collected with very little debris.

The washings collected from animals after a week or 10 days on the diet show little change. There is, however, an approximate 50% decrease in their number.

Significant changes in morphology of the cells collected occur when definite signs of the deficiency are being noted grossly in the eye. Increasing numbers of non-nucleated cells appear. In the third or fourth week of the deficiency these cells become more abundant. Distinct cellular details fade, and the cells become extremely variable in their staining qualities. Some take the stain very deeply whereas others appear as phantoms or outlines. As the deficiency progresses large masses are formed and are associated with copious amounts of debris.

Histological Observations of the Eye.   The normal corneal epithelium in the rat (Fig. 1) is five or six cell layers in thickness. The basal layer rests upon the substantia propria and contains cuboidal cells quite uniform in size with large darkly staining nuclei and a pale less distinct cytoplasm. Mitotic figures are quite often found in this layer. Cells of the upper layers are flattened, spindle-shaped, and have distinct nuclei. The surface of this tissue is smooth and moist. Occasionally an entire cell may detach itself and become free in the conjunctival sac (Fig. 1). These sloughed cells appear normal.

The histological picture of the progressing deficiency is most revealing. The cytoplasm of cells in the intermediate layers have indistinct outlines. The nuclei seem to shrink leaving a space between them and the underlying cytoplasm. The most obvious change is at the surface (Fig. 2). It is now irregular and the sloughed cells are more dense.

As the deficiency advances distinct changes occur. The cells of the basal layer are arranged in an irregular line and are less active. The intermediate cell layers blend into a homogeneous zone. This area is pale staining, the nuclei within it appear clear with prominent nucleoli. The surface, too, seems to be less cellular. Some deep staining particles appear in the transitional zone between the intermediate layers and the surface (Fig. 3).

The corneal epithelium of a rat with a "full" deficiency is shown in Figs. 4 and 5. The morphological features are quite definite and reproducible. The total thickness has decreased. The basal layer is reduced to a single layer of cells with rounded or flattened nuclei. Mitotic figures are few. The clear intermediate zone is very apparent; it blends into an area containing fine keratohyalin granules. These granules increase in size near the surface. They line up in rough irregular zones to form dark bands (Fig. 4) and converge into platelike sheets of keratin. The dark bands are separated from each other by clear zones and thus form alternately dark and light layers.

INFLUENCE OF VITAMIN A ON THE DEFICIENT STATE

Effect on Mitosis in vitro

In the control group of tissues which received no vitamin A in the incubating flasks (see zero concentration of vitamin A in Figs. 18–20) the mitotic index of epidermis, corneal and tracheal epithelial of vitamin A-deficient animals is significantly less than that of epithelia from normal animals. The mitotic index of the epithelia is not significantly altered due to the presence of the aqueous dispersion vehicle. However, the addition of 10 μg of vitamin A to the in vitro system causes an increase in the mitotic index of all epithelia (normal and A-deficient) when compared with the zero concentration controls. An even greater increase in epithelial mitotic index of all tissues is observed when 100 μg of the vitamin is added to the system (Figs. 18–20).

In most instances, the presence of high concentrations of vitamin A (1000 or 10,000 μg) significantly lowers the mitotic index of both the normal and A-deficient epithelia as compared with the zero concentration controls. In several instances, however, these high con-

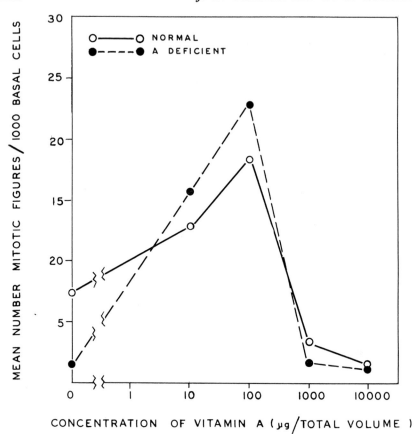

Fig. 18. The effect of vitamin A on the mitotic activity of epidermis *in vitro*.

centrations of vitamin A do not show statistically significant lowered values for mitotic index. This is mainly true for epidermis and tracheal epithelium taken from vitamin A-deficient animals (Figs. 18 and 20). However, the number of mitotic figures present in the control samples of these epithelia are extremely low at the outset and toxic doses of the vitamin can probably do little to cause further depression of the mitotic index.

Effect of Vitamin A on Cornea

The application of vitamin A to the conjunctival sac will maintain the corneal epithelium in a normal state if it is introduced at an

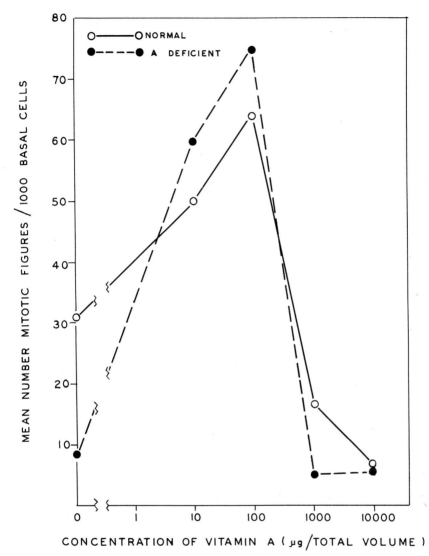

Fig. 19. The effect of vitamin A on the mitotic activity of corneal epithelium *in vitro*.

early stage of the deficiency or when the eye is normal. Doses of 1 μg of the vitamin given every 48 hours and maintained for seven applications is sufficient to do this. This amount of vitamin is not capable of reversing the systemic effect of deficiency. This is shown

by the fact that the untreated eye will develop symptoms of the
deficiency as described previously.

Introduction of small doses of vitamin A into the eye after A deficiency symptoms of the eye are rather severe, results in increased
activity of the basal layer with a subsequent increase in the total

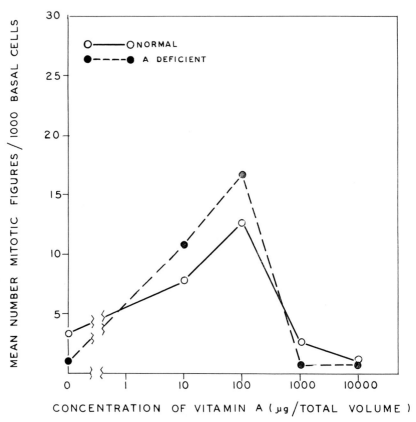

Fig. 20. The effect of vitamin A on the mitotic activity of tracheal epithelium *in vitro*.

thickness (Fig. 11). The newly forming cells at the base of the epithelium seem to push the keratinized elements to the surface and
give the structure an appearance of having two layers. Cells in the
intermediate layers are large and clear and intercellular spaces are
apparent. Intercellular bridges are easily demonstrated in these

treated tissues. The other eye of the same animal not treated with vitamin A but with the vehicle only, Fig. 10, shows distinct signs of the deficiency. Note the irregular appearance of the cell layers and the appearance of leucocytes throughout the tissue. Some cells show extreme hypertrophy. Leucocytic invasion of the tissues is common in late deficiency.

Discussion

VITAMIN A-DEFICIENT STATE

Although it is true that many animals will become vitamin A deficient quite easily, it is difficult to measure the degree of deficiency produced. Many rats will show signs of deficiency such as stationary weight in as little as thirty days. Other animals can remain on an A-deficient diet for months and never progress in the deficiency. Our previous work taught us that rats cannot remain grossly deficient for more than 48 hours; that is, without some liver and/or circulating vitamin A. Apparently some animals can remain in a partially deficient state and become stabilized, with very little stores and no intake of vitamin A.

Clarke and Todd (1957) feel that an excellent criterion for the A-deficient state is the development of a cornified vaginal smear in the castrated female rat. They describe a technic for its use as a biological assay for vitamin A. These studies as well as our own on corneal epithelia lead us to believe that some kind of biological test is necessary which could ascertain the degree of A deficiency in each experimental animal individually without regard to the length of time that the animal has been deprived of the vitamin. No mere recording of the time that an animal has been subjected to a deficient diet can be taken as an index of the degree of deficiency established.

RELATION OF MITOTIC RATE TO THE DEFICIENCY AND TO KERATINIZATION

Our studies of mitosis in vitamin A-deficient rats demonstrate that there is a significant fall in mitotic index of epithelia concomitant with a decrease in serum vitamin A. This is not in agreement with the results of Wolbach and Howe (1933), who found an increase in mitotic activity with A deficiency, and Friedenwald *et al.* (1945), who claimed that the number of mitoses per 1000 basal cells in the corneal epithelium of vitamin A-deficient rats was not significantly different from that of rats on a normal diet.

The results of the *in vitro* experiments reported here show that the administration of physiologic amounts of vitamin A causes a significant increase in the mitotic index of epithelia, whereas high toxic doses of the vitamin significantly diminish mitotic activity in A-deficient and normal rats. This is in agreement with the results of Lawrence and Bern (1958) and Alov (1957), who found that vitamin A greatly stimulated cell division and increased the mitotic activity of epithelia. It also appears that in considering mitotic indexes, the vitamin A-deficient epithelia are more responsive to the action of the vitamin A than are normal epithelia.

A study of the influence of vitamin A on the mitotic activity of epithelial tissues may lead us to a better understanding of the process of keratinization. In the cornea only basal cells proliferate, and as they move into the upper layers, they become more differentiated. The sloughed product is cellular and normal squamous cells can be found in washings from normal eyes. In the deficient state, the proliferation of cells in the basal layer is reduced, and this decreased rate has an effect upon the differentiation of the sloughed product. The rate of differentiation is slower, or the total period is lengthened, or both. Cells remain in the tissue longer, and the final product is more differentiated.

OTHER EFFECTS OF VITAMIN A

It would be difficult or impossible to explain all the effects of vitamin A on its ability to influence the proliferation of epithelial cells. Certain changes occur in epithelial tissues of the vitamin A-deficient animal that seem to have little to do with mitotic rate. The pseudostratified columnar epithelium of the trachea can no longer be maintained in the deficient state, and it soon reverts to the stratified squamous type (Fig. 16) resembling the normal or even deficient corneal epithelium. The corneal epithelium, normally stratified squamous when denied the vitamin, undergoes significant changes as well. Under these new metabolic conditions it produces keratin—a process usually reserved for the cells of the epidermis. The function of the skin, too, is affected; hair no longer grows, sebaceous glands degenerate, and keratin accumulates. Certainly, all these changes cannot be attributed to a change in mitotic rate.

Cells that have been subjected to vitamin A in tissue culture behave differently from cells not so exposed. The skin of the chick embryo is no longer capable of producing keratin but instead changes to produce a cuboidal or columnar epithelium. According to Weiss and James (1954) a single exposure to vitamin A for as little as one-half hour can bring about this transformation. They feel that this is a true inductive change since even after repeated transfers through media without added vitamin A the tissue remains altered. The classical work of Fell and Mellanby (1953) went a step farther, producing a mucous-secreting epithelium from stratified squamous epithelium after exposure to vitamin A in tissue culture. (See also Lawrence et al., 1960; Lawrence and Bern, 1960; Bern and Lawrence, this volume.)

It is obvious from such work that vitamin A can alter the characteristics of epithelial tissues. Epithelial tissue is capable of change under different environmental states. Under optimal conditions of nutrition and support an epithelial tissue could advance to produce a columnar or cuboidal mucous secreting tissue. In the absence of vitamin A or under some other adverse condition the tissue may revert to a morphologic pattern that could be supported by less favorable conditions than is necessary to maintain its normal characteristics.

Vitamin A certainly plays a part in the nutrition of a tissue; this is related to the ability of the tissue to proliferate and can be called the supportive role of the vitamin. Vitamin A can also bring about a progressive alteration in form under optimal nutritional conditions. It is postulated that in the absence of vitamin A, a regressive alteration in form takes place. Vitamin A is necessary to retain the morphological status of certain epithelial tissues and in its absence the tissue regresses to a form that is capable of being supported under the less favorable nutritional conditions. One cannot maintain a keratin-producing cornea in the presence of vitamin A. When vitamin A is introduced into the conjunctival sac of an animal with a progressive deficiency, the cornea does not produce keratin. It remains normal even though a systemic deficiency is established.

Summary and Conclusions

Epithelial tissues of the rat were studied after a vitamin A deficiency had been established. The progress of the deficiency in the corneal epithelium was followed and discussed in relation to the production of keratin. The following conclusions can be drawn from the work reported or reviewed.

1. The direct utilization of the vitamin by the tissue is demonstrated since a normal cornea can be maintained in a systemically A-deficient rat with repeated doses of vitamin A.

2. Vitamin A stimulates the mitotic activity of both normal and deficient tissues *in vitro* and *in vivo* when administered in moderate dosage. In high toxic doses it can inhibit the mitotic activity.

3. The rate at which cells proliferate seems to be a factor in the keratinization process.

4. Even in grossly deficient animals, a keratin-producing cornea is not maintained if vitamin A is administered topically.

Acknowledgment. We should like to express our thanks to Dr. Albert Sobel, of the Brooklyn Jewish Hospital, for his help in the initial phases of some of this work.

REFERENCES

Alov, I. A. 1957. Cell division and vitamin A. *Byull. Eksptl. Biol. Med.,* 43: 76–80.

Bern, H. A. 1954. Histology and chemistry of keratin formation. *Nature,* 174: 509–511.

Bern, H. A., Elias, J. J., Pickett, P. B., Powers, T. R., and Harkness, M. N. 1955. The influence of vitamin A on the epidermis. *Am. J. Anat.,* 97: 419–488.

Bern, H. A., Harkness, D. R., and Blair, S. M. 1955. Radioautographic studies of keratin formation. *Proc. Natl. Acad. Sci. U.S.,* 41: 55–60.

Bessey, O. A., Lowry, O. H., Brock, M. J., and Lopez, J. A. 1946. The determination of vitamin A and carotene in small quantities of blood serum. *J. Biol. Chem.,* 166: 177–188.

Bullough, W. S. 1954. A study of the hormonal relations of epidermal activity *in vitro*. I. Technique. *Exptl. Cell Research, 7*: 176–185.

Bullough, W. S. 1954. A study of the hormonal relations of epidermal activity *in vitro*. II. Insulin and pituitary growth hormone. *Exptl. Cell Research, 7*: 186–196.

Bullough, W. S., and Johnson, M. 1951. A simple technique for maintaining mammalian epidermal mitosis *in vitro*. *Exptl. Cell Research, 2*: 445–453.

Carleton, A., and Steven, D. 1943. Keratosis follicularis: a study of four cases. *Arch. Dermatol. u. Syphilis, 48*: 143–150.

Clarke, P. M., and Todd, P. E. 1957. Some observations on the biological assay of vitamin A and its precursors by vaginal-smear method. *Brit. J. Nutrition, 11*: 173–184.

Crawford, G. H. 1951. Treatment of acne. In *Modern Medicine Annual*. Minneapolis, Minn. P. 316.

Davidson, D. M., and Sobel, A. E. 1949. Aqueous vitamin A in acne vulgaris. *J. Invest. Dermatol., 12*: 221–228.

Dublin, W. B., and Hazen, B. M. 1948. Relation of keratosis seborrheica and keratosis senilis to vitamin A deficiency. *Arch. Dermatol. u. Syphilis, 57*: 178–183.

Eddy, W. H., and Howell, J. L. 1939. Topical application of vitamin A: Efficiency judged by growth stimulation. *N.Y. State J. Med., 39*: 406–410.

Fell, H. B., and Mellanby, E. 1953. Metaplasia produced in cultures of chick ectoderm by high vitamin A. *J. Physiol. (London), 119*: 470–488.

Fell, H. B., Mellanby, E., and Pelc, S. R. 1954. Influence of excess vitamin A on the sulphate metabolism of chick ectoderm grown *in vitro*. *Brit. Med. J., 2*: 611.

Fisher, R. A. 1936. *Statistical Methods for Research Workers*. Oliver and Boyd Ltd., Edinburgh. Pp. 126–128.

Flesch, P. 1952. Inhibition of keratin formation with unsaturated compounds. *J. Invest. Dermatol., 19*: 353–363.

Flesch, P. 1953. Studies on the mode of action of vitamin A. *J. Invest. Dermatol., 21*: 421–434.

Flesch, P., and Goldstone, S. B. 1952. Local depilatory action of unsaturated compounds. The effect of human sebum on hair growth. *J. Invest. Dermatol., 18*: 267–287.

Frazier, C. N., and Marmelszadt, W. L. 1948. Vitamin A deficiency and the skin in retrospect: A historical search into nosological antecedents. *Bull. Hist. Med., 22*: 766–795.

Frazier, C. N., and Hu, E. K. 1931. Cutaneous lesions associated with deficiency of vitamin A in man. *A.M.A. Arch. Internal Med., 48*: 507–514.

Friedenwald, J. S., Buschke, W., and Morris, M. E. 1945. Mitotic activity and wound healing in the corneal epithelium of vitamin A-deficient rats. *J. Nutrition, 29*: 299–308.

Goldschmidt, M. 1915. Experimenteller Beitrag zur Aetiologie der Keratomalacie. *Arch. Ophthalmol., 90*: 354–366.

Greenberg, R., Cornbleet, T., and Demovsky, R. 1954. Conversion of carotene to vitamin A by sebaceous glands. *A.M.A. Arch. Dermatol., 76*: 17–23.

Harris, L. J., Innes, J. R. M., and Griffith, A. S. 1932. On the pathogenesis of avitaminosis A: vitamin A as the anti-keratinizing factor. *Lancet, 223*: 614–617.

Heimer, C. B., Grayzell, H. B., and Kramer, B. 1951. Local therapy in dermatoses of the newborn infant. *Arch. Pediat., 68*: 382–387.

Jewell, H. A., Taube, H., Nicholls, M. E., and Lehmann, R. A. 1957. Action of vitamin A on the skin following intracutaneous injection. *Proc. Soc. Exptl. Biol. Med., 96*: 162–165.

Kahn, R. H. 1954a. Effect of locally applied vitamin A and estrogen on the rat vagina. *Am. J. Anat., 95*: 309–336.

Kahn, R. H. 1954b. Effect of œstrogen and of vitamin A on vaginal cornification in tissue culture. *Nature, 174*: 317.

Kahn, R. H., and Bern, H. A. 1950. Antifolliculoid activity of vitamin A. *Science, 111*: 516–517.

Lahiri, K. D., and Scandrett, F. J. 1954. Vitamin A in acne vulgaris. *J. Indian Med. Assoc., 23*: 247–249.

Lawrence, D. J., and Bern, H. A. 1958. On the specificity of the response of mouse epidermis to vitamin A. *J. Invest. Dermatol., 31*: 313–325.

Lawrence, D. J., and Bern, H. A. 1960. Mucous metaplasia and mucous gland formation in keratinized adult epithelium *in situ* treated with vitamin A. *Exptl. Cell Research, 21*: 443–446.

Lawrence, D. J., Bern, H. A., and Steadman, M. G. 1960. Vitamin A and keratinization. Studies on the hamster cheekpouch. *Ann. Otol. Rhinol. & Laryngol., 69*: 645–660.

Leitner, Z. A., and Moore, T. 1956. Vitamin A and skin disease. *Lancet, 251*: 262–265.

Lowe, J. S., Morton, R. A., and Harrison, R. G. 1953. Aspects of vitamin A deficiency in rats. *Nature, 172*: 716–719.

Lynch, F. W., and Cook, C. D. 1947. Acne vulgaris treated with vitamin A. *Arch. Dermatol. u. Syphilis, 55*: 355–357.

Montagna, W. 1954. Penetration and local effect of vitamin A on the skin of the guinea pig. *Proc. Soc. Exptl. Biol. Med., 86*: 668–672.

Mori, M. 1904. Ueber den sogenanten Hikam (Xerosis conjunctivae infantum) eventuell keratomalacie. *Jahrb. Kinderheilk., 59*: 175–195.

Moult, F. H. 1943. Histopathology of rat skin in avitaminosis A. *Arch. Dermatol. u. Syphilis, 47*: 768–777.

Sabella, J. D., Bern, H. A., and Kahn, R. F. 1951. Effect of locally applied vitamin A and estrogen on rat epidermis. *Proc. Soc. Exptl. Biol. Med.,* 76: 499–503.

Sherman, B. S., Sobel, A. E., and Parnell, J. P. 1959. The influence of vitamin E on the percutaneous absorption of vitamin A. *J. Invest. Dermatol., 32*: 577–580.

Sobel, A. E., Parnell, J. P., Sherman, B. S., and Bradley, D. K. 1958. Percutaneous absorption of vitamin A. *J. Invest. Dermatol., 30*: 315–331.

Sobel, A. E., Rosenberg, A., Bradley, D. K., and Parnell, J. P. 1955. Transfer of topically applied vitamin A through the skin. *Voeding, 16*: 773–778.

Sobel, A. E., Rosenberg, A., Bradley, D. K., Parnell, J. P. 1956. Percutaneous and oral absorption of vitamin A. *A.M.A. Arch. Dermatol.,* 73: 388–394.

Sobel, A. E., Sherman, B. S., and Parnell, J. P. 1959. The influence of concentration on the percutaneous and oral absorption of vitamin A. *J. Invest. Dermatol., 32*: 569–576.

Sobel, A. E., and Snow, S. D. 1947. The estimation of serum vitamin A with activated glycerol dichlorchydrin. *J. Biol. Chem., 171*: 617–632.

Straumfjord, J. V. 1943. Vitamin A: Its effect on acne. *Northwest Med.,* 42: 219–225.

Studer, A. 1953. Zur Frage der Angriffsorte von Compound E (Cortison). Eine experimentelle Studie. *Z. ges. exptl. Med., 121*: 287–418.

Studer, A., and Frey, J. R. 1949. Ueber Hautveränderungen der Ratte nach grossen oralen Dosen von Vitamin A. *Schweiz. med. Wochschr.,* 79: 382–384.

Sulzberger, M. B., and Baer, R. L. 1949. *Yearbook of Dermatology and Syphilis.* Yearbook Publishers, Chicago, Ill. P. 14.

Weiss, P., and James, R. 1954. Vitamin A and skin keratinization *in vitro:* Experimental dissociation of induction and realization phases in cytodifferentiation. *Science, 119*: 587.

Wolbach, S. B., and Howe, P. R. 1925. Tissue changes following deprivation of fat-soluble A vitamin. *J. Exptl. Med., 42*: 753–778.

Wolbach, S. B., and Howe, P. R. 1928. Vitamin A deficiency in the guinea pig. *Arch. Pathol. Lab. Med., 5*: 239–253.

Wolbach, S. B., and Howe, P. R. 1933. Epithelial repair in recovery from vitamin A deficiency. *J. Exptl. Med., 57*: 511–526.

7

Effect of Environmental Factors on the Physical Characteristics of the Stratum Corneum

Irvin H. Blank

The Research Laboratories of the Department of Dermatology, Harvard Medical School, at the Massachusetts General Hospital, Boston, Massachusetts.

The greater part of this symposium is devoted to discussion of the dynamics of keratin formation in three tissues, the skin, the oral mucous membranes, and the teeth. Other anabolic processes which accompany formations of the keratins render these tissues chemically complex. In the skin, the tissue which is thus formed is the stratum corneum. This brief contribution deals with the influence of certain environmental factors on the physical characteristics of this tissue. Consideration of mucous membranes and teeth will be left to other contributors. The environmental factors to be discussed here are: (1) relative humidity of the environment, (2) detergents* and water, and (3) ultraviolet irradiation.

Relative Humidity of the Environment

It can be shown that the flexibility of the stratum corneum is a function of its water content (Blank, 1952). A thin sheet of stratum corneum can be removed without difficulty from the skin of the

---

* The term "detergents" as used here includes both soap and the newer synthetic detergents.

palms or soles, particularly if friction has previously caused thickening. If such a sheet is allowed to dry out, it becomes inflexible and brittle. Its flexibility will return if the sheet is held in water, but not if it is held in oil or grease. Water is the only known plasticizer of the stratum corneum. As long as the stratum corneum remains *in situ*, it is usually sufficiently hydrated to be somewhat flexible. It will be shown, however, that the degree of hydration is a function primarily of the relative humidity of the environment, not of the amount of water this tissue has received from the underlying tissues.

The stratum corneum is formed as the living cells of the epidermis die and become more or less dehydrated. The outer lamellae of the stratum corneum, i.e., the stratum corneum disjunctum, are separated from living epidermal cells by a dense layer, the stratum corneum compactum, which lies at the base of the cornified epithelium. This layer contains the barrier which prevents dehydration of underlying tissues (Blank, 1953). Fortunately for general physiological equilibrium, the stratum corneum compactum of man and corresponding structures in the integument of animals are less permeable to water than are most other biological membranes. Since the purpose of the barrier of the stratum corneum compactum is to prevent loss of water from underlying tissues, it necessarily retards passage of water from the body pool to the distal lamellae of the stratum corneum.

In addition to the small amount of water which the stratum corneum disjunctum can receive from within the body by slow diffusion through the barrier, it can also receive water from the sweat glands. Over most areas of the body, however, the sweat glands are inactive when the environmental temperature is below about 85° F. Consequently, under ordinary environmental conditions, the greater part of the water which the stratum corneum receives from the general body pool must have reached that tissue by diffusion through the barrier. Diffusion through the barrier is very slow; diffusion through the stratum corneum disjunctum to the cutaneous surface, on the other hand, is relatively fast, and once water has reached the cutaneous surface, it evaporates rapidly under most environmental conditions.

Since the stratum corneum disjunctum usually loses water to the environment more rapidly than it receives water from the underlying tissues, this layer tends to dry out, and it would probably become relatively dehydrated, but for the fact that it contains hydrophilic materials. Under most environmental conditions, these hydrophilic materials are thought to prevent complete evaporation of the water received from the underlying tissues. Also, if the relative humidity of the environment rises, the stratum corneum may take up water from the environment until equilibrium is reached.

The water content of the stratum corneum is determined more by environmental conditions than by the factors which control the water content of other body tissues. When the relative humidity of the environment is low, the moisture content of the stratum corneum at equilibrium is low. One must remember, however, that not the relative humidity of the *general environment,* but rather the relative humidity of the *micro-environment* may be what determines the moisture content at equilibrium. By "micro-environment" is meant the very thin, relatively static layer of air immediately adjacent to the skin. Under most conditions, the relative humidity of the micro-environment is probably higher than that of the air at some distance from the skin.

Since the moisture content of the stratum corneum influences its flexibility and its moisture content is a function of the relative humidity, the relative humidity of the environment indirectly affects the flexibility of the stratum corneum. As its flexibility decreases, the stratum corneum is more likely to flake and fissure. Roughness and poor flexibility are characteristics of dry or "chapped" skin.

Contact with Water and with Aqueous Solutions of Detergents

At least some of the hydrophilic components of the stratum corneum are water-soluble (Spier and Pascher, 1959). These water-soluble substances are removed by frequent contact with water, and the water-holding capacity of the tissue is thereby reduced. It is probable that aqueous solutions of detergents remove a larger proportion of the water-soluble components of the stratum corneum than does water alone (Blank and Shappirio, 1955). If they do, they may further lower the water-holding capacity of the stratum corneum. There is as yet no evidence that the synthetic detergents remove more hydrophilic compounds from the stratum corneum than does soap.

After the cornified epithelium has been treated with polar lipid solvent, water can remove a much larger proportion of the water-soluble substances than it could before such treatment, and the water-holding capacity becomes comparatively low (Blank, 1953).

Although, as has been pointed out, the flexibility of the stratum corneum is a function of its water content, factors other than water content may influence the flexibility of this tissue. Two equally hydrated pieces of stratum corneum may differ so far as flexibility is concerned. As water-soluble substances are removed from the stratum corneum by water or aqueous solutions of detergents, the decrease in flexibility of the stratum corneum is more marked than the simultaneous small decrease in water-holding capacity would lead one to expect. The reason for this is not yet understood.

Under normal conditions, the lamellae of the stratum corneum disjunctum are not firmly attached to each other, and the sebum present on the skin may perhaps exert a weak cementing action which keeps the cutaneous surface relatively smooth. When aqueous detergent solutions are placed on normal skin, they remove some of the surface sebum. In addition, the water causes hydration and consequent swelling of the lamellae. Subsequent evaporation of water from the skin, in turn, causes the lamellae to shrink. The removal of the sebum and the alternate swelling and shrinking of the lamellae cause these lamellae to be even less adherent to each other than normally. Also the surface lamella fractures. These processes roughen the surface of the skin.

It is evident, therefore, that when solutions of cleansing agents have been in contact with the skin, the stratum corneum disjunctum will become less flexible and less compact, and its surface will become rough. If the stratum corneum becomes sufficiently brittle, it may break when flexed, and fissures may result. All these changes are signs and symptoms of "dry skin."

Ultraviolet Irradiation

The physical characteristics of the stratum corneum depend to some extent on its thickness; other factors being equal, the thicker the stratum corneum, the less flexible it is. The thickness of this layer is a function of the rate at which it receives new cells from the underlying tissue and the rate at which it sheds old cells from its outer surface.

Many factors influence the rate of cellular mitosis in the basal layer of the epidermis and thus affect the rate at which cells reach the stratum corneum. Almost any form of injury accelerates the rate of mitosis in the basal layer. Ultraviolet radiation sufficient to produce mild inflammation causes injury which may be expected to increase the mitotic rate. Little is known about the rate of shedding after such mild exposure to ultraviolet radiation. The extensive shedding which follows a severe sunburn is not being considered. It is known that one of the responses to ultraviolet radiation is a thickening of the epidermis (Mïescher, 1930); therefore, temporarily at least, the balance between the rate of shedding and the rate of mitosis must have changed. The thickened stratum corneum serves, in turn, to help protect the skin from further injury from ultraviolet irradiation.

Periods of increased ultraviolet irradiation often coincide with periods in which the relative humidity of the environment is comparatively high. Therefore, even though the stratum corneum may thicken, its water content may simultaneously increase sufficiently to offset the loss of flexibility due to thickening. In a dry climate, the changes resulting from ultraviolet irradiation may cause symptoms resembling those of dry skin.

Summary

Since the stratum corneum of the skin normally loses water to the environment faster than it receives water from the underlying tissues, it tends to dry out. It is kept from complete dehydration by the presence of hydrophilic substances. Its water content at equilibrium is a function primarily of the relative humidity of the micro-environment of the skin. The water content of the stratum corneum is one of the factors which control its flexibility.

Some of the hydrophilic substances in the stratum corneum are water-soluble and are removed by contact with water or with aqueous detergent solutions. Sebum also is removed by contact with such solutions. Swelling as a result of hydration, with subsequent shrinking from dehydration, tends to disrupt the lamellae of the stratum corneum disjunctum. The lamellae break and the surface becomes rough. Repeated exposure to ultraviolet radiation causes thickening of the stratum corneum.

REFERENCES

Blank, I. H. 1952. Factors which influence the water content of the stratum corneum. *J. Invest. Dermatol., 18:* 433–440.

Blank, I. H. 1953. Further observations on factors which influence the water content of the stratum corneum. *J. Invest. Dermatol., 21:* 259–269.

Blank, I. H., and Shappirio, E. B. 1955. The water content of the stratum corneum. III. Effect of previous contact with aqueous solutions of soaps and detergents. *J. Invest. Dermatol., 25:* 391–401.

Miescher, G. 1930. Das Problem des Lichtschutzes und der Lichtge-wöhng. *Stahlentherapie, 35:* 403–443.

Spier, H. W., and Pascher, G. 1959. Physiologie der Hautoberfläche. *Aktuelle Probleme der Dermatologie, 1:* 1–46.

8

Keratinization of the Oral Mucosa

Julia Meyer and Herman Medak
Division of Oral Pathology, College of Dentistry, University of Illinois, Chicago

The Concept of Degrees of Keratinization

Whereas in the skin parakeratosis has a pathological connotation denoting an interference with the keratinizing process, it has been considered a normal variant in the gingiva. It occurs in approximately 60 to 70% of gingival biopsy specimens, the remainder going to fully keratinized or to nonkeratinizing epithelium (Figs. 1–3). Absence of keratinization, though usually thought of as another normal variant, has sometimes been associated with underlying inflammation.

We have recently reexamined the relations between keratinization and inflammation, which in the gingiva is the rule rather than the exception, and also the relations between keratinization and glycogen, which is frequently found deposited in gingival epithelium. Because the gingiva is regionally diversified and inflammation often is confined to small areas, we divided the epithelium into subregions and evaluated the variables locally. We found that full keratinization is rare in the presence of either glycogen or of inflammation, and does not occur at all when inflammation is severe or when glycogen is present in larger quantity.

The status of unkeratinized regions of gingiva was similarly clear-cut. Keratinization was absent where inflammation was severe and/or large amounts of glycogen were present. An inverse relation between keratinization and glycogen had been observed in other

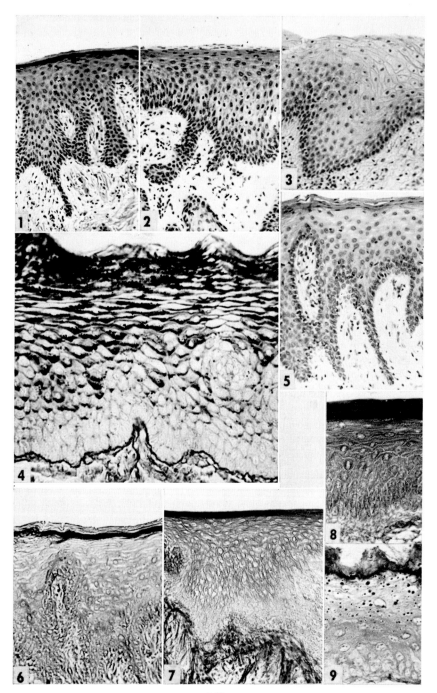

140

epithelia. Our study showed that the epithelium of the region adjacent to the gingiva, the alveolar mucosa, contained glycogen in all specimens and was always unkeratinized (Fig. 4). We concluded from our regional breakdown that inflammation and glycogen deposition both tend to interfere with the keratinizing process, that full keratinization occurs in the absence of such interference, and that nonkeratinization is the opposite extreme. Parakeratosis appeared to occupy a place between these extremes. It occurred in 79% of 234 regions, in conjunction with quite a range of glycogen concentrations as well as with inflammation of differing severity, and often in the absence of both.

In hematoxylin and eosin preparations, the parakeratotic edge looked alike in all specimens, but on the basis of staining with Mallory's connective tissue stain, parakeratosis could be divided into two types. With this mixture, the keratin layer of fully keratinized epithelium stains in a bright shade of red or orange-red. In parakeratinized regions, the keratin layer either stained in this same shade of red, or else was divided into an inner layer which stained red, and an outer one which stained blue, Figs. 5–7). The blue shade of the outer layer is due to the aniline blue of the staining mixture and appears also in the cytoplasm of the cells in the Mal-

---

Figs. 1, 2, and 3. Regions of normal human gingiva illustrating three types of keratinization. Hematoxylin and eosin, ×110. 1, region showing ortho-keratinization; 2, region showing complete parakeratinization; 3, unkeratinized region.

Fig. 4. Human alveolar mucosa, stained for demonstration of glycogen (PAS). Note the deposits of glycogen in all but the deepest layers of cells of this unkeratinized epithelium (×180).

Figs. 5, 6, and 7. Regions of human gingiva showing two types of parakeratinization (×110). 5 and 6, incomplete parakeratinization: 5, hematoxylin and eosin; 6, the same specimen, stained with Mallory's triple connective tissue stain, showing divided staining of the parakeratinized layer. 7, complete parakeratinization—the same specimen as in 2, stained with Mallory's triple connective tissue stain. Note the uniform staining of the parakeratinized edge in this specimen in contrast to that in the specimen shown in 5 and 6.

Figs. 8 and 9. Regions of oral mucosa of the mouse, stained with Mallory's triple connective tissue stain: 8, palate (×215); 9, cheek (×290). Note the uniform staining of the keratin layer in the palatal epithelium in contrast to the divided staining of the keratin of the buccal epithelium. In the latter, note the diffuse distribution and huge size of the keratohyaline granules, and the great proportion of extragranular cytoplasm.

pighian layers. This type of staining was seen in one-third of the parakeratotic regions of gingiva and appeared regularly at the transition between the unkeratinized alveolar mucosa and the keratinized gingiva. We noted that inflammation seemed to be more severe or glycogen more abundant in gingival regions with divided keratin staining. We therefore separated these specimens from those in which the keratin layer stained as a whole, and now obtained clearer correlations with inflammation and glycogen.

When we arranged the specimens in the order: fully keratinized, parakeratotic undivided, parakeratotic divided, unkeratinized, we found with each new class an increase in the incidence and quantity of glycogen and in the incidence and degree of inflammation. Parakeratosis with uniform keratin staining was compatible with small quantities of glycogen and/or slight inflammation; parakeratosis with divided keratin staining with larger quantities of glycogen and/or moderate inflammation, with these two factors to some extent interchangeable.

It appeared, then, that glycogen and inflammation, two factors which are inversely related to keratinization and which can be quantitatively varied, did not have an all-or-none effect, but inhibited keratinization by degrees. Conversely, it appeared that the keratinizing process is not an all-or-none event, but occurs in various degrees. We concluded that four *degrees* rather than four *types* of keratinization were present in human gingiva.

Parakeratosis with divided keratin staining was called "incomplete parakeratosis," because it fitted between nonkeratinization and regular parakeratosis.

Occurrence of Incomplete Orthokeratinization

In the mouse and other rodents, no parakeratotic and no unkeratinized regions occur. Hematoxylin and eosin preparations show the entire oral epithelium to be orthokeratinized and the keratin layer to stain in the same shade everywhere. The recognition of regional differences in keratinization was forced on us belatedly, when we attempted to study the effects of tobacco smoke.

The keratin layer of different regions of mouse oral epithelium, when stained with Mallory's connective tissue stain and also with a number of other staining mixtures such as Buzzi's "eleidin" stain or Unna's method for tonofibrils, stains in one of two ways. In some regions, for instance the palate, the whole stratum corneum stains like hair keratin, whereas in others, for instance the cheek, only the deeper portion of the keratin stains in this way, and the superficial layer takes up the same component as the Malpighian layer (Figs. 8–9). These two types of staining behavior of the keratin layer are the same as those of the keratin in parakeratotic as against incompletely parakeratotic regions of human gingiva. If one could show that the difference between differently staining regions in the rodents has the same significance as that between differently parakeratinized regions in the human, this would mean that not only parakeratosis but also orthokeratosis occurs in different degrees of completeness.

The idea that keratinization might advance to a higher degree in the palate than in the cheek is given support by the microscopic differences in the cellular layers of the epithelium in the two regions. The palatal epithelium conforms closely to the mushroom-shaped pattern of cell differentiation resulting from the progressive flattening of the cells which Pinkus has diagrammed for epidermal epithelium (Fig. 11). It is true that tonofibrils are not as clearly identifiable in the mouse or hamster as in human palatal epithelium and that the cells are not spaced as far apart. Intercellular bridges are therefore shorter and the nodes of Bizzozero less marked. There is, however, no difficulty in identifying these microscopic signs of fibrillar keratin precursors in the epithelium of the palate. In the epithelium of the cheek, the cells do not undergo a reduction in height, nor does their horizontal diameter increase. Tonofibrils and intercellular bridges appear to be absent. The cells abut on one another. With most stains, cell membranes or boundaries cannot be made out (Fig. 10).

Perhaps the most striking difference is in the eleidin system. The keratohyaline granules of the palatal epithelium are formed in a compact layer of squamous cells following many layers of spinous cells (Fig. 11). They are minute in size, exceedingly numerous, and occupy the whole cytoplasmic space. In the cheek, granule

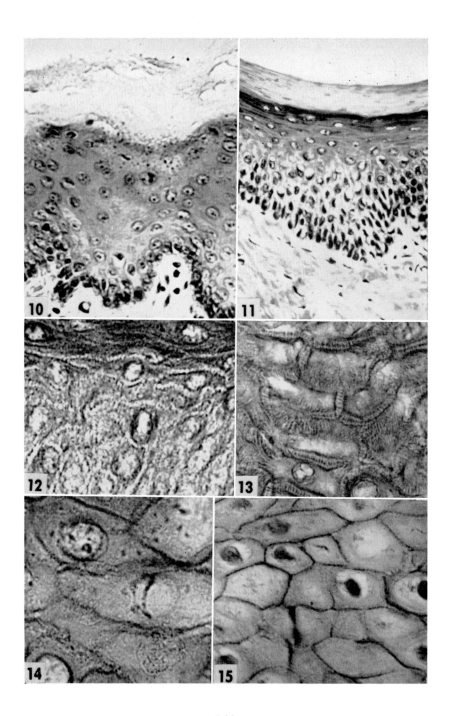

formation begins close to the basal layer. The granules gradually increase in number as well as in size; in fact, many in the peripheral granular cells attain a huge size. The bulk of the cytoplasm, however, is outside of granules even in these cells (Figs. 9, 10). The small ratio of surface to volume of the large granules in conjunction with the rapid turnover of the cheek epithelium may mean that biochemical processes of keratization are not carried to completion. In addition, the extragranular cytoplasm may become a non-keratinous admixture to the keratin layer.

All these differences point to be probability that the fibrillar as well as the "eleidin" precursors of keratin are more distinctly elaborated in the palate than in the cheek, and that it is this difference which is reflected in the staining behavior of the stratum corneum of the two regions. This supports the idea that orthokeratinization as well as parakeratosis occur in two degrees of completeness.

Significance of Incomplete Keratinization

Oral histologists divide the mucosa of the human oral cavity into masticatory, specialized, and lining regions. Masticatory mucosa, the lining of the hard palate and the gingiva, is said to be keratinized so as to be resistant to masticatory forces. Lining mucosa is found in the floor of the mouth and the cheeks, regions which are thought to be under no masticatory stress and can therefore afford to be

---

Figs. 10 and 11. Regions of oral mucosa of the mouse stained with hematoxylin and eosin: 10, buccal epithelium—note the absence of intercellular spaces and cell boundaries and the failure of the peripheral cells to flatten out, also the looseness of the keratin (×350); 11, palatal epithelium—note intercellular spaces and progressive flattening of cells between basal layer and stratum corneum, compactness of the granular layer and minute size of the keratohyaline granules, and also the compact packing of the keratin (×375).

Figs. 12–15. Regions of oral mucosa, stained with Mallory's stain: 12, palate of mouse (×720); 13, keratinized region of human gingiva (×825); 14, cheek of mouse (×975); 15, human alveolar mucosa (×825). Note that the intercellular spaces are similarly wide in completely orthokeratinized regions of mouse and human oral cavity, although the bridges are less distinct in the mouse and in contrast the contiguity between adjacent cells in the incompletely orthokeratinized region of the mouse and similarly in the unkeratinized region of the human.

unkeratinized. The oral histologist has not discussed the oral cavity of the rodent, which is everywhere lined by keratinized epithelium. He might wish to say that mastication in these animals leads to a different distribution of stresses, and he might point out that absolutely and relatively the thickest layer of keratin is found in the occlusal plane of the cheek (Fig. 10). It is quite true that we usually think of an epithelium with a thicker layer of keratin as being more highly keratinized. But this is reasoning by analogy with epidermal regions such as palm or sole, and our findings suggest that it is not applicable to oral mucosa.

Despite its thick layer of keratin, the epithelium of the cheek of the mouse is strikingly similar to the unkeratinized epithelium of the human cheek or that of any other unkeratinized part of the human oral cavity. The unkeratinized human alveolar mucosa and a keratinized portion of human gingiva show the same contrast in their patterns of histodifferentiation as do the buccal and the palatal epithelium of the mouse.

Figures 12 and 13, illustrating sections of mouse palatal epithelium and of keratinized human gingiva prepared with Mallory's staining mixture, show the similarity in the distant spacing of the cells in these two epithelia. Figure 14, showing the keratinized cheek epithelium of the mouse, and Fig. 15, showing the unkeratinized human alveolar mucosa, illustrate an even more striking similarity in the contiguous spacing of the cells and in the absence of stainable material in the cells of these two epithelia.

Comparison of the cell sizes again shows the similarity of the members of each pair, and the impressive contrast between the pairs. We have made a quantitative comparison of the cell densities in the human alveolar mucosa and attached gingiva in a series of 65 biopsies and found the cells of the alveolar mucosa larger in every specimen where a comparison could be made. The average cross-sectional area was about 220 sq microns for the alveolar mucosa and 135 sq microns for the attached gingiva. We have also compared cell sizes in the buccal and palatal epithelium of the mouse. The mouse has smaller cells than the human, but the difference goes in the same direction and is of the same order. We found the size in the cheek to average about 100 sq microns and in the palate 71 sq microns.

One can sum this up by saying that there is little similarity between the palatal and the buccal epithelium of the mouse despite the fact that both are keratinized and a close similarity between the cheek of the human and the cheek of the mouse, despite the fact that the one is not keratinized at all, whereas the other has the thickest keratin layer of all regions of the mouse oral cavity. Perhaps it is not surprising to find that in those regions of the oral cavity in which in the course of evolution keratinization was given up in some species, the ground was prepared for it, for these regions already had many of the features of an unkeratinizing epithelium.

This leaves us with the question of whether the keratinization in such regions is really of a lower degree and confers a lower degree of protection than the keratin of the palate. In order to answer this, we have compared the rates of surface wear in mouse cheek and palate. We have determined the mitotic rates and from these made estimates of the turnover times of palatal and buccal epithelium. These turned out to be 24 days for the palate and 16 days for the cheek. The thickness of the cellular layers averaged 65 microns for the palate and 116 microns for the cheek. From these figures we computed the rates of growth and found the palatal epithelium to grow at 2.7 microns per day and the buccal epithelium at 7.2 microns, that is, nearly three times as rapidly as that of the palate. Surface wear should be faster in the same proportion. This result substantiates our previous interpretation that the morphological features simulating unkeratinized epithelium and the poor elaboration of keratin precursors lead to a less stable type of keratin.

We have concluded that orthokeratinization, like parakeratosis, can proceed to different degrees of completion, that "incomplete orthokeratinization," like incomplete parakeratinization, is an incomplete process of keratinization, and that it leads to an unstable end product.

We may well ask why the epithelium of the cheek should be such as to produce a type of keratin which cannot resist the surface forces in the area and therefore requires rapid replacement. The answer seems to us related to the fact that the cheek is a muscular organ and must have a mucosa which adjusts to the changing size of the surface which it lines. The different degree of stretch rather than the different degree of stress seems to underlie the difference between the epithelium of the cheek and that in the hard palate, which is tightly fixed to dense connective tissue and bone. In the keratin itself the difference is clearly reflected in the tightly packed, stretched, thin, parallel lamellae in the palate (Figs. 8, 11) and the randomly oriented loose flakes in the cheek (Figs. 9, 10).

Dr. Blank (p. 133) has pointed out that the flexibility of the keratin layer is dependent on its capacity to hold water. We have considered incomplete keratinization in much the same light, that is, as producing a keratin layer of high potential water content. It may be that the initial dehydration is not as complete or that keratinization is less complete in some other respect, which permits free reentry of water from the oral cavity into the keratin superficial to the transitional layers.

The picture we have presented is sketchy and overschematic in concentrating on only the two extreme types of epithelium in the mouse. We should add that one finds incomplete orthokeratinization not only in mucosa which lines muscles but also in what may really be protected sites, for instance the soft palate. We do not know the rate of growth of the human cheek in comparison with that of the palate and therefore cannot say whether for the human oral cavity the traditional concept that unkeratinized epithelia are found at protected sites might remain valid, despite our contradictory findings in the rodents. Incomplete orthokeratinization occurs in the human oral cavity as well as that of the rodent. The circumstances under which it occurs fit our interpretation of its being a less advanced type than complete orthokeratinization.

Acknowledgment. The authors wish to express their appreciation to Mr. William Winn, biological photographer, for his help in preparing the illustrations.

REFERENCES*

Marwah, A. S., Weinmann, J. P., and Meyer, J. 1960. Effect of chronic inflammation on the epithelial turnover of the human gingiva. *A.M.A. Arch. Pathol.,* 69: 147–153.

* This presentation discusses in a general context some aspects of the work on oral mucosa which was carried out under the leadership and participation of the late J. P. Weinmann, who died while this symposium was being planned. The following references to published work indicate his share in this work.

Meyer, J., Medak, H., and Weinmann, J. 1960. Mitotic activity and rates of growth in regions of oral epithelium differing in width. *Growth,* *24:* 29–46.

Weinmann, J. P., and Meyer, J. 1959. Types of keratinization in the human gingiva. *J. Invest. Dermatol., 32:* 87.

Weinmann, J. P., Meyer, J., Mardfin, D., and Weiss, M. 1959. Occurrence and role of glycogen in the epithelium of the alveolar mucosa and of the attached gingiva. *Am. J. Anat., 104:* 381–402.

Weinmann, J. P., Meyer, J., and Medak, H. 1960. Correlated differences in granular and keratinous layers in the oral mucosa of the mouse. *J. Invest. Dermatol., 34:* 423–431.

Weiss, M. D., Weinmann, J. P., and Meyer, J. 1959. Degree of keratinization and glycogen content in the uninflamed and inflamed gingiva and alveolar mucosa. *J. Periodontology, 30:* 208–218.

9

Studies on Odontogenic Cyst Epithelium

KERATINIZATION IN ODONTOGENIC CYSTS*

J. J. Pindborg, H. P. Philipsen, and J. Henriksen
Department of Oral Pathology, Royal Dental College, Copenhagen, Denmark

In most texts the epithelial lining of dental cysts is described as a stratified squamous epithelium. It is the general opinion that the epithelia in radicular and follicular (dentigerous) cysts do not differ to a great extent. However, Thoma (1954) claims that in the epithelium of follicular cysts there is often an evidence of "pseudo-keratosis," a process which Thoma does not define further. On the other hand, Tiecke et al. (1959) find occasionally an overproduction of keratin by the epithelial lining in radicular cysts. Gorlin (1957) reports 200 cases of mandibular dentigerous cysts among which he finds keratinization in 32%. Among 72 epithelial-lined radicular cysts, Langer (1947) finds 4.2% exhibiting keratinization. Recently, Shear (1960) has reported on 22 cysts which he calls "primordial" and which, according to the author, form about 10% of all epithelial-lined cysts of the jaws.

Shear postulates that primordial cysts show a number of histological features which, when considered together, render the diagnosis of a primordial cyst fairly certain. One of these features is the presence of a keratinized or parakeratinized layer on the surface of the epithelium.

* This work was supported by a grant from the P. Carl Petersen's Foundation.

Several case reports of keratinized cysts (so-called cholesteatomas) have appeared in the literature, and an analysis of these cases is given by Philipsen (1956), who suggests the term *odontogenic keratocysts* regardless of the cyst being of the follicular (dentigerous), radicular (periodontal) or residual type.

It appears from the literature that few statistical data are available as to the frequency of keratinization in different types of odontogenic cysts. Furthermore, the keratinization process has not been discussed in detail.

The purpose of the present investigation has been to determine: (1) the frequency of keratinization in dental cysts, (2) the aptitude of the keratinization to develop in follicular rather than in radicular or residual cysts, (3) the type of keratinization occurring in odontogenic cysts, (4) the existence of transitional stages between fully keratinized cysts, and (5) a possible correlation between PAS-positive material and keratinization.

Material and Methods

The 1952–1960 files of The Department of Oral Pathology, Royal Dental College, Copenhagen* were reviewed and 791 odontogenic cysts found. The material comprised 98 follicular, 611 radicular, and 82 residual cysts, Table I. A residual cyst is understood to be a cyst which is located in an area of the alveolar process where teeth have been extracted. Excluded were all cases of fissural cysts and soft tissue cysts. Cases which showed keratinization to a large extent were registered as odontogenic keratocysts. Cases with small scattered foci of keratinization were not included. Fortunately, if an odontogenic cyst shows keratinization, it is in most cases a widespread process, thus eliminating the difficult task of deciding whether a cyst belongs to one group or the other.

Among the 791 cysts, 28 or 3.5% were odontogenic keratocysts. Table I shows the distribution of these 28 cysts according to the cyst type. A control material of 33 nonkeratinized cysts (16 with little or no inflammation and 17 with marked inflammation in the cyst wall) and the 28 odontogenic keratocysts were subjected to

* Supplemented with the private files of the senior author.

Table I. Distribution of Cyst Types and Incidence of Keratinization

Type	Distribution		Incidence of Keratinization			
	Number	Per Cent	Number ♀	♂	Total	Per Cent
Follicular	98	12.4	3	4	7	7.1
Radicular	611	77.2	3	4	7	1.1
Residual	82	10.4	8	6	14	17.1
Total	791	100.0	14	14	28	3.5

the following stains: hematoxylin-eosin, Mallory's connective tissue stain (Weinmann and Meyer, 1959), and periodic acid Schiff reagent with and without diastase pretreatment.

Results

FREQUENCY OF KERATINIZATION IN ODONTOGENIC CYSTS

According to clinical and radiological diagnoses, the 28 odontogenic keratocysts were divided into follicular, radicular, and residual cysts. Table I shows the distribution according to type of cyst and the incidence of keratinization in each of the cyst types. It is remarkable that 17.1% of the residual cysts are keratinized. It should also be noted that keratinization occurs within radicular cysts (in 1.1%) although it is more rare than in follicular cysts, among which 7.1% are keratinized. There is no difference as to sex distribution. Nineteen of the odontogenic keratocysts were found in the mandible and 9 in the maxilla.

TYPE OF KERATINIZATION IN ODONTOGENIC KERATOCYSTS

The epithelium in odontogenic keratocysts has a characteristic appearance. It is frequently very thin consisting of 5 to 6 rows of cells and shows no rete pegs (Fig. 1). The basal cell layer is well defined with either columnar or cuboidal cells. The stratum spinosum is very scanty and sometimes a direct transition takes place from the basal cell layer into the superficial layer. When stratum spinosum is present many cells show vacuolization in this layer.

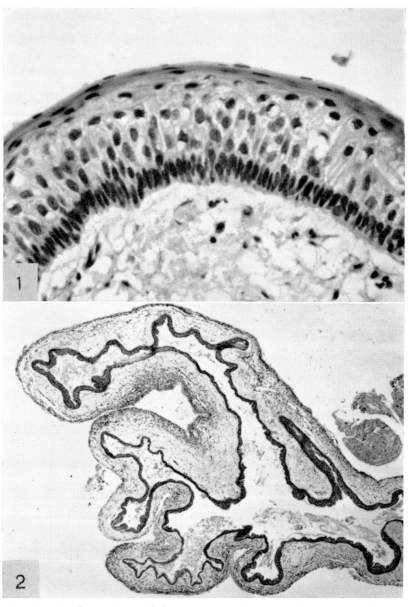

Fig. 1.   Parakeratotic epithelium in an odontogenic keratocyst. Note the accentuated basal cell layer and the missing rete pegs. Hematoxylin-eosin, ×405.

Fig. 2.   Low-power magnification of odontogenic keratocyst. Note wavy surface of epithelium in some areas. Hematoxylin-eosin, ×35.

The superficial layer of the epithelium, i.e., the layer toward the lumen of the cyst, is either wavy or straight (Fig. 2).

The keratinization occurring in the odontogenic keratocyst is of the parakeratotic type in 26 out of 28 cysts. The remaining two cases show an orthokeratosis (Fig. 3) according to the terminology used by Weinmann *et al.* (1960). The parakeratotic layer is not ordinarily preceded by a granular layer (Figs. 1 and 3). In this material, however, a granular layer is present in two cysts showing parakeratosis. In some of the cysts the formation of keratin is so abundant that it fills up the entire cystic cavity. When mixed with cystic fluid, this content has a characteristic semisolid cheesy consistency. Other cysts show only small flakes of keratin. The connective tissue adjacent to the epithelium shows little or no signs of inflammation in odontogenic keratocysts.

By means of the Mallory's connective tissue stain the keratinized layers are clearly brought out in a strikingly red color which contrasts with the underlaying blue-stained cellular layers. Besides demonstrating the ortho- and parakeratotic keratinizations, the Mallory stain is also useful in revealing incomplete parakeratosis (Weinmann and Meyer, 1959). This type of keratinization was found in only 3 of the 28 odontogenic keratocysts. In some of the odontogenic keratocysts, small nonkeratinized areas are seen. In the Mallory-stained sections these areas, close to keratinized epithelium, show a yellow color which seems to indicate the presence of a prekeratinizing stage.

In the material of 33 nonkeratinized cysts, originally evaluated in hematoxylin-eosin-stained sections, isolated islands of red-stained keratin were found in 6 cases. In addition, signs of incomplete keratinization were seen in 2 cases. In another 2 cases quite extensive areas of yellow-stained epithelium were noted. However, the findings in the Mallory-stained nonkeratinized cysts did not disclose keratinization to such an extent that the diagnosis be changed to keratocyst.

OCCURRENCE OF PAS-POSITIVE MATERIAL

In the epithelium of *odontogenic keratocysts* two types of PAS-positive material were ascertained.

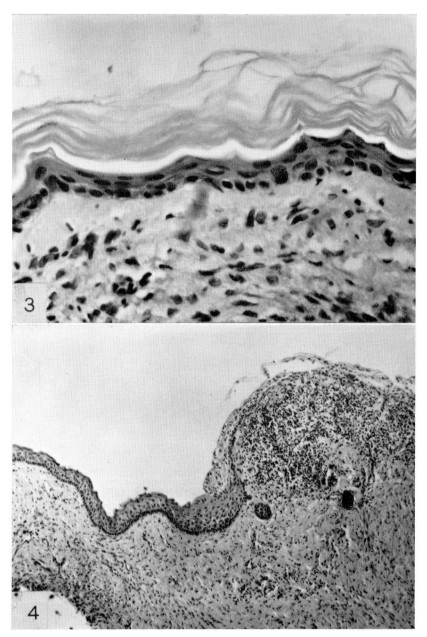

Fig. 3.   Orthokeratosis of epithelium in odontogenic keratocyst. Note the extreme narrow epithelium. Hematoxylin-eosin, ×405.

Fig. 4.   Transition of unkeratinized epithelium into parakeratotic epithelium in an odontogenic keratocyst. The transition occurs when inflammation disappears. Hematoxylin-eosin, ×88.

First, the use of the diastase incubation showed intraepithelial glycogen to occur in small amounts in the Malpighian layer mostly in the areas where the epithelium is thick.

Secondly, cells containing a strong PAS-positive, diastase-resistant material were found quite frequently within the different strata of the epithelium in nonkeratinized areas. There seems to exist two types of cells characterized by their content of PAS-positive, diastase-resistant material. In hematoxylin-eosin stain, the first type has the appearance of mucous cells, while the second cell type shows a yellowish granular cytoplasm like macrophages. The cells of the latter type may also be found in adjacent connective tissue and in the cyst lumen.

Finally, a rather weak PAS-positive, diastase-resistant material in the superficial layer of the epithelium was found corresponding to the keratinized areas.

In the *nonkeratinized* cysts more glycogen was found than in the odontogenic keratocysts. However, no consistency was found in correlating the amount of glycogen with the degree of inflammation. The incidence of PAS-positive, diastase-resistant cells of the mucous type was the same in nonkeratinized cysts and keratocysts. The diffusely occurring PAS-positive, diastase-resistant material in the superficial epithelium of keratocysts was not seen in nonkeratinized cysts.

Discussion

This investigation has shown that keratinization may occur in both follicular, radicular, and residual cysts, with the highest incidence (17.1%) in residual cysts. Gorlin (1957) found an incidence of 32% with keratinization in follicular cysts, but in his material maxillary cysts were omitted. Our finding of 1.1% odontogenic keratocysts among the radicular cysts is the same magnitude that Langer (1947) found: 4.2%. We cannot accept Shear's postulate that the occurrence of this special keratinized epithelium indicates that the cyst is primordial. A residual cyst may be radicular as well as follicular in origin and it would even be extremely difficult to prove that all residual cysts are follicular cysts. However, it is interesting to note that Shear (1960) found the same ratio for mandible/maxilla as was found in this investigation, namely, 2:1.

It was a constant finding that keratinization in dental cysts occurred only when the adjacent connective tissue showed little or no signs of inflammation. It can be assumed that when the inflammation in a cyst wall subsides, conditions are created for the process of keratinization (Fig. 4). This concept is in accordance with Weinmann and Meyer's findings (1959) in the gingiva, where they demonstrated that parakeratosis is most often seen together with little or no inflammation. The rather rare occurrence of incomplete parakeratosis in dental cysts, as compared with the quite high incidence in the gingiva, may be explained by certain properties of the cyst fluid. When discussing the incomplete parakeratosis in the gingival epithelium, Weinmann and Meyer (1959) assume that the outer strip of keratin comes under the influence of saliva or other factors in the oral environment and is thereby altered so as to lose its keratin-like staining properties. The modifying factors may not be present to the same extent in cyst fluid.

With regard to the presence of glycogen in the cyst epithelium, our findings are in agreement with the findings in the gingival epithelium, i.e., that the glycogen is found located in the Malpighian layer and that inflammation tends to cause an accumulation of glycogen.

The strong PAS-positive, diastase-resistant cells of the mucous type were found to be equally frequent in nonkeratinized areas of odontogenic keratocysts and in nonkeratinized cysts of both types. Apparently, these cells do not play a role in the keratinization process. However, it should be mentioned that Lawrence et al. (1960) found mucous metaplasia in the stratified squamous epithelium of hamster cheek pouch after topical application of high doses of vitamin A. It may indicate that environmental factors, i.e., the cyst fluid, may contribute to the differentiation of the cyst epithelium.

When discussing the significance of the diffuse and weak PAS-positive, diastase-resistant material occurring in the zone of keratinization, reference should be made to Stoughton and Wells

(1950), who also found a mucopolysaccharide, resistant to amylase, in the hornified layer of the skin.

At the moment, no explanation can be given as to why in some cases the cyst epithelium undergoes keratinization. The high incidence among residual cysts may give some hints because these cysts may be conceived as cysts of long standing. In time the inflammation has subsided, and thus the basis for development of keratinization has been created.

Summary

Among 791 odontogenic cysts keratinization was found in 3.5%. The incidence of keratinization was highest among residual cysts (17.1%) and lowest among the radicular cysts (1.1%); 7.1% of the follicular cysts showed keratinization. The ratio of odontogenic keratocysts in mandible and maxilla was 2:1. The Mallory stain was used to demonstrate the keratinization which in most cases was parakeratotic. Areas of incomplete parakeratosis were rarely found. Simultaneously with the keratinization, a PAS-positive, diastase-resistant material was found.

It is assumed that keratinization occurs when inflammation subsides, and that this process is seen in cysts of long standing such as the residual ones.

REFERENCES

Gorlin, R. J. 1957. Potentialities of oral epithelium manifest by mandibular dentigerous cysts. *Oral Surg. Oral Med. Oral Pathol., 10*: 271.

Langer, H. 1947. Histologische Studien an Bälgen von Zahnzysten. Z. *Stomatol., 44*: 102.

Lawrence, D. J., Bern, H. A., and Steadman, M. G. 1960. Vitamin A and keratinization. *Ann. Otol. Rhinol. & Laryngol., 69*: 645.

Philipsen, H. P. 1956. On keratocysts in the jaws. *Tandlaegebladet, 60*: 963.

Shear, M. 1960. Primordial cysts. *J. Dent. Assoc. S. Africa, 15*: 211.

Stoughton, R., and Wells, G. 1950. A histochemical study on polysaccharides in normal and diseased skin. *J. Invest. Dermatol., 14*: 37.

Thoma, K. H. 1954. Oral Pathology, 4th ed. C. V. Mosby & Company, St. Louis, Mo.

Tiecke, R. W., Stuteville, O. H., and Calandre, J. C. 1959. *Pathologic Physiology of Oral Disease.* C. V. Mosby & Company, St. Louis, Mo.

Weinmann, J. P., and Meyer, J. 1959. Types of keratinization in the human gingiva. *J. Invest. Dermatol., 32:* 87.

Weinmann, J. P., Meyer, J., and Medak, H. 1960. Correlated differences in granular and keratinous layers in the oral mucosa of the mouse. *J. Invest. Dermatol., 34:* 423.

10

Extracellular Position of Enamel[*]

Michael L. Watson

Departments of Pathology and Radiation Biology, School of Medicine and Dentistry, The University of Rochester, Rochester, New York

A number of electron microscope studies describing the fine structure of forming dental enamel have been published (Watson and Avery, 1954; Fearnhead, 1958; Quigley, 1959), but none of these has shown clearly the precise relation of enamel matrix to the ameloblast. The present communication will present evidence to show that incisal enamel in the rat, like dentin, is extracellular.

Methods

Lower incisors were dissected from the mandibles of 200-gram Sprague-Dawley stock rats under ether anesthesia and placed in fixative. The blood supply was interrupted for about 5 minutes before fixation was started. Fixation was for 1 hour at 0–5°C in 1% OsO_4 buffered to pH 7.3 with veronal acetate containing sucrose and the buffer strength was one-tenth that recommended by Caufield (1957). Tissues were dehydrated in ethyl alcohol and embedded in butyl methacrylate. Sections were stained 30 minutes in lead hydroxide (Watson, 1958) and mounted on carbon-filmed

[*] These investigations were performed in part under contract with the United States Atomic Energy Commission at the University of Rochester, Atomic Energy Project, Rochester, New York, and in part with funds provided by Research Grant CY-3589 (C3) from the National Institutes of Health, United States Public Health Service. Except for conformity to style of this monograph, the original findings here summarized were first published in the *Journal of Biophysical and Biochemical Cytology*, 7 (3): 489–492 (1960).

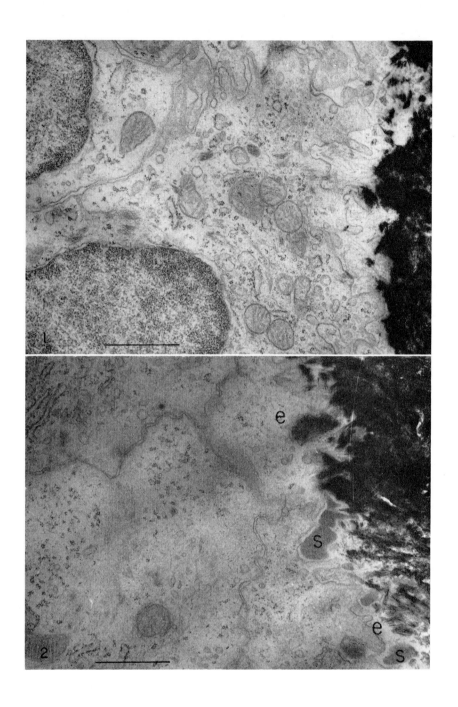

162

grids and sandwiched (Watson, 1957) with evaporated carbon. Microscopy was done with the Siemens Elmiskop I operating at 80 kv with a 50-micron objective aperture.

Results

The essential part of these observations lies in determining the position of the forming enamel with respect to the cell membrane. It was found that the cell membrane was difficult to see clearly unless the section was sandwiched, and it is for this reason, presumably, that earlier work has failed to reveal these details.

The rat incisor in cross section is approximately triangular, one side of the triangle representing the labial aspect of the curved tooth. The enamel coats only this surface and is in the form of a ribbon which becomes much attenuated and finally disappears at its edges. In sections cut transversely to the axis of the tooth, it is possible to follow stages of enamel formation by proceeding medially from the edge of the enamel ribbon, where no enamel has been deposited, to the center of the ribbon, where the enamel is thickest. A series of micrographs demonstrating this near the base of the tooth is shown in Figs. 1 to 4.* At the extreme edge of the enamel

* Figures 1 to 4 show a series of sections cut transversely to the axis of the lower incisor of the rat near the base of the tooth. Figure 1 is taken at the edge of the ribbon of enamel which coats only the labial aspect of the incisor, and Figs. 2, 3, and 4 are taken at points progressively more medial to this. All sections were stained with lead hydroxide for 30 minutes and were sandwiched with carbon. The calcified portion of the tooth appears at the right of each micrograph and the cytoplasm of the ameloblasts is on the left.

Fig. 1. The only calcified material appearing at the edge of the enamel ribbon is represented here by the dense image of dentin. No enamel has been deposited. Portions of two ameloblasts are shown. The ameloblast cell membrane follows a complicated path on the dentinal side of the cells and is spaced from the dentin by a region containing fine filaments and some uncalcified collagen. Nuclei are close to the dentin, and all parts of the cytoplasm contain the usual cell components such as mitochondria and endoplasmic reticulum (×20,000).

Fig. 2. Very early stages in enamel formation are detectable. Masses of stippled material (s) are present between calcified dentin and the cell membranes of the ameloblasts. At one or two points (e) the beginnings of enamel calcification can be seen. Ameloblast nuclei are no longer close to the dentinal end of the cells, and the cytoplasm at that end now contains relatively few mitochondria and little endoplasmic reticulum (×20,000).

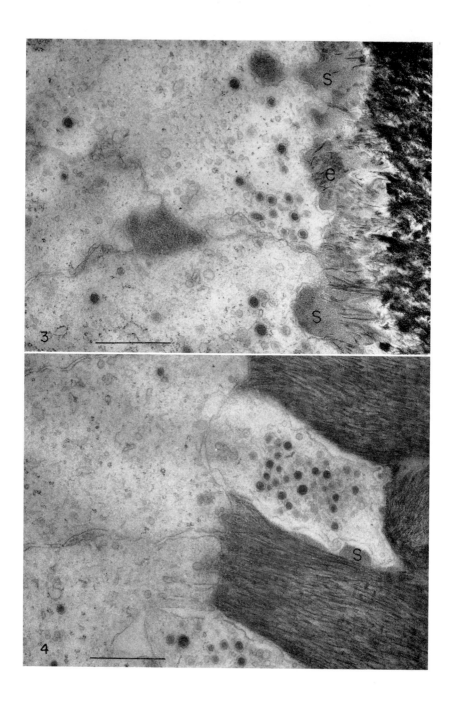

164

(Fig. 1) essentially only dentin is present to represent the tooth substance. The surface of the ameloblasts is not in contact with the dentin, but follows a somewhat tortuous path, often approaching the dentin closely but in general leaving a well-marked space between dentin and cell membrane. Within the ameloblasts, cytoplasmic constituents such as mitochondria and endoplasmic reticulum lie close to the end of the cells toward the dentin. Adhesion plates or desmosomes are frequently seen between adjacent ameloblasts. The cells are not columnar and the nuclei are close to the dentin.

A short distance inward from the edge of the enamel ribbon (Fig. 2) three changes are apparent. Nuclei are no longer close to the dentin, a zone containing little or no endoplasmic reticulum or mitochondria is present within the ameloblasts at the dentinal end, and the beginnings of enamel formation are discernible. Between the cell membrane and the dentin can be seen globular masses of finely stippled material as well as occasional areas of calcification which are recognizable as enamel by virtue of the length of the dense profiles of inorganic material. Both the globular masses and the early enamel are outside the cell membrane.

At a still more advanced stage in development (Fig. 3) forming enamel entirely covers the dentin. Dense, ribbon-shaped profiles can be seen embedded in finely stippled material like that described above. Extracellular, globular masses of this material are also seen between the ameloblasts at some distance from the enamel surface.

Fig. 3.　Dentin is now completely covered by a rudimentary layer of enamel (e). Large amounts of stippled material (s) are present with the lathe-shaped elements of calcifying enamel embedded within it. Other masses of stippled material are noticeable at some distance from the enamel. The enamel and stippled material are separated from the ameloblast cytoplasm by the cell membrane. Within the ameloblast are numerous, rather dense, membrane-enclosed globules which might represent granules of enamel matrix before secretion (×20,000).

Fig. 4.　Enamel is assuming the characteristic, highly ordered appearance of enamel rods in the inner enamel of the rat. Indentations in the serrated surface of the forming enamel are occupied by extensions of ameloblasts. The ameloblast cytoplasm is at all points covered by cell membrane and is not directly in contact with enamel. At some points stippled material (s) can be seen in contact with the enamel and apparently continuous with the matrix surrounding the dense, lathe-shaped elements (×20,000).

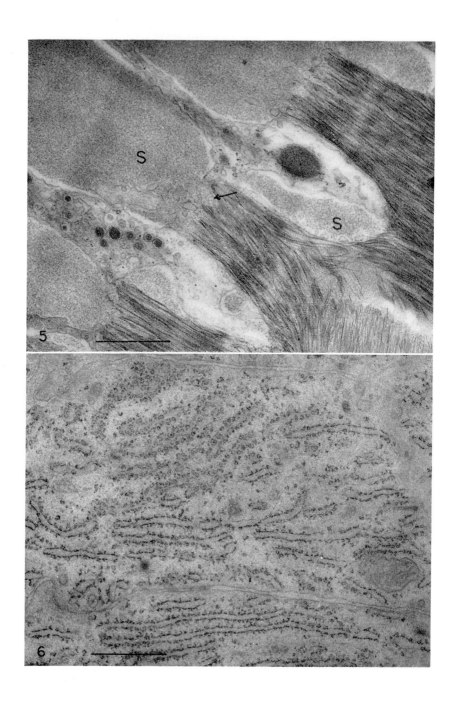

166

The dense profiles are oriented approximately at right angles to the dentino-enamel junction which represents one point of their termination. The other point of termination of the profiles is at or close to the cell membrane. Various small, spherical globules are present in the clear zone of cytoplasm of the ameloblasts which are suggestive of the finely granular material outside. These may be precursors of enamel matrix in the form of secretion granules.

Near the center of the enamel sheath (Fig. 4) the structure has taken on the characteristic appearance of enamel rods when viewed in sections (Watson and Avery, 1954). In this area only small amounts of the finely stippled material are present and are continuous with the areas of the enamel containing ribbon-shaped elements. Both the stippled material and the enamel proper are separated from the cytoplasm of the ameloblasts by the cell membrane. Numerous small, spherical globules of the type described above are present in parts of the clear zone of ameloblast cytoplasm close to the enamel.

Masses of the stippled material described above, although not always present, are a frequent finding in the rat incisor at later stages of inner enamel formation (Fig. 5). Whether their presence bears any systematic relation to enamel development we cannot say. This material does not represent enamel matrix, once calcified, but subsequently decalcified by the staining procedure, because it can also be found in unstained sections (Watson, unpublished).

One further point of interest which should be emphasized is the large amount and high degree of development in the ameloblast of the rough-surfaced endoplasmic reticulum, that is, endoplasmic

Fig. 5. The surface of forming inner enamel at a much more advanced stage than that shown in the previous micrographs. At this stage, very large masses of stippled material (s) are present in the rat. The material is continuous with enamel matrix (arrow), but, like the enamel, is extracellular. Attenuated arms of ameloblast cytoplasm extend between the masses of stippled material and terminate within pockets in the surface of the forming enamel (×20,000).

Fig. 6. Cytoplasm of the ameloblast at some distance from the forming enamel. Larger amounts of endoplasmic reticulum are present having a dense investment of ribonucleoprotein particles. The particles are characteristically arranged in the ameloblast in short spirals. The high development of rough-surfaced endoplasmic reticulum suggests that the ameloblast is strongly secretory (×20,000).

reticulum bearing ribonucleoprotein (RNP) particles. Greatly extended elements are oriented predominately parallel to the long axis of the columnar cells (Fig. 6). The rough-surfaced endoplasmic reticulum occupies a major portion of the cytoplasmic volume of the ameloblast. It is interesting to note that most of the RNP particles are arranged in circles or spirals similar to formations described by Palade (1955) in other cells.

Discussion

The stippled material which is present in variable amounts at the surface of forming inner enamel in the rat incisor appears to be continuous with the organic matrix in which the enamel crystallites are embedded. Sometimes large, globular masses of this material can be found; however, what relation it may bear to various granules and vacuoles (Saunders *et al.*, 1942), which have been described in light microscope studies, is not clear. One may presume either that this represents the enamel matrix precursor in the process of deposition as suggested by Fearnhead (1958) or that it is organic material lost from the enamel as calcification proceeds. Radioautographic studies by Leblond *et al.*, (1955) show that injected S^{35}-labeled sulfate is earliest deposited in greatest amounts at the surface of the enamel. This suggests, therefore, that this stippled material which is sometimes present in such large amounts has only recently been synthesized and that it is not organic matrix leaving the enamel. Whatever its role, it is continuous with and shares with the enamel a location which is extracellular.

The presence of large amounts of highly organized, rough-surfaced endoplasmic reticulum gives the ameloblasts an outstanding morphological feature of secretory cells and in this respect puts them in a class with pancreatic acinar cells and active fibroblasts. Cells in which the major synthetic product remains intracellular, such as normoblasts, the cortical cells of hair (Birbeck and Mercer, 1957b,c), or the cells which finally make up the cornified epithelium of the tongue, although containing many RNP particles possess relatively little endoplasmic reticulum. Ameloblasts, though of ectodermal origin, thus differ from some other ectodermal cells in that morphologically they resemble strongly secretory cells. The product which is of a "structural" nature does not resemble hair and cornified epithelium in that the enamel is not made up of cornified cells but is wholly extracellular.

These observations disagree with earlier work of ours and of others which suggested that enamel might be intracellular (Watson and Avery, 1954; Quigley, 1959; Fearnhead, 1958). The present finding that enamel is extracellular was reached because it was possible by sandwiching sections between high-melting materials to prevent certain local distortions under the electron beam and thus to observe clearly the cell membrane near the enamel. It seems reasonable to presume that the secretory features of the ameloblast cytoplasm are connected with the elaboration of enamel matrix.

If, indeed, enamel is to be regarded as a eukeratin as has been reported in several studies (Stack, 1954, 1955; Battistone and Burnett, 1956), we have in this case the first example to the author's knowledge of a protein that may be found in either extra- or intracellular locations. In this connection, we should stress that by intracellular we mean present within the cytoplasm and not surrounded by a membrane. Thus, muscle protein and hemoglobin would properly be called intracellular, whereas pancreatic digestive enzymes while existing within the cell boundary as secretion granules, are surrounded by a membrane (Palade, 1956), and would here be considered as extracellular.

At the present time there appear to be two qualitatively different ways in which RNP particles are associated morphologically with proteins undergoing synthesis. On the basis of present evidence, it is not unreasonable to assume that some proteins such as pancreatic digestive enzymes are formed within membranous vesicles which have on the outer surface of the membrane an investment of attached RNP particles. Other proteins such as hemoglobin or hair and epidermal keratins appear to form "nake" within the cytoplasm in regions close to RNP particles, but in the absence of any interposed membrane. Since the roles of ribonucleic acid (RNA) and of RNP particles in protein synthesis are far from clear, it would be fruitless to speculate on possible effects of a membrane enclosing the synthesizing product; however, these observations and considerations do suggest that enamel protein may well differ in important respects from other eukeratins. The presence in enamel of proline and hydroxyproline, much glycine, and little cystine is pointed out by Battistone and Burnett (1956) as not typical of the keratins.

Summary

Developing incisal enamel of the rat was examined with the electron microscope in sections stained with heavy metal and sandwiched so as to reveal details hitherto unvisualized because of low contrast and destruction by the electron beam. The fact that a cell membrane always lies between the ameloblast and the enamel indicates that enamel is extracellular and not intracellular. Implications of this with regard to the possible keratinous nature of enamel matrix are discussed.

REFERENCES

Battistone, G. C., and Burnett, G. W. 1956. Studies of the composition of teeth. IV. The amino acid composition of human enamel protein. *J. Dental Research, 35*: 260–262.

Birbeck, M. S. C., and Mercer, E. H. 1957a. The electron microscopy of the human hair follicle. I. Introduction and the hair cortex. *J. Biophys. Biochem. Cytol., 3*: 203–214.

Birbeck, M. S. C., and Mercer, E. H. 1957b. The electron microscopy of the human hair follicle. II. The hair cuticle. *J. Biophys. Biochem. Cytol., 3*: 215–222.

Birbeck, M. S. C., and Mercer, E. H. 1957c. The electron microscopy of the human hair follicle. III. The inner root sheath and trichohyaline. *J. Biophys. Biochem. Cytol., 3*: 223–230.

Caufield, J. B. 1957. Effects of varying the vehicle for OsO_4 in tissue fixation. *J. Biophys. Biochem. Cytol., 3*: 827–830.

Fearnhead, R. W. 1958. Comparative observations on the ultra-structure of the inorganic and organic components of dental enamel. *Program of Fourth International Conference on Electron Microscopy*, Berlin (Abs.). Pp. 353–357.

Leblond, C., Belanger, L. F., and Greulich, R. C. 1955. Formation of bones and teeth as visualized by radioautography. *Ann. N.Y. Acad. Sci., 60*: 631–659.

Palade, G. E. 1955. A small particulate component of the cytoplasm. *J. Biophys. Biochem. Cytol., 1*: 59–68.

Palade, G. E. 1956. Intracisternal granules in the exocrine cells of the pancreas. *J. Biophys. Biochem. Cytol.*, 2: 417–421.

Quigley, M. 1959. Electron microscopy of developing enamel matrix in the Syrian hamster. *J. Dental Research*, 38: 180–187.

Saunders, J. B., Nuckolls, J., and Frisbie, H. E. 1942. Amelogenesis. *J. Am. Coll. Dentists*, 9: 107–136.

Stack, M. V. 1954. Organic constituents of enamel. *J. Am. Dental Assoc.*, 48: 297–306.

Stack, M. V. 1955. The chemical nature of the organic matrix of bone, dentin and enamel. *Ann. N.Y. Acad. Sci.*, 60: 585–595.

Watson, M. L. 1957. Reduction of heating artifacts in thin sections examined in the electron microscope. *J. Biophys Biochem. Cytol.*, 3: 1017–1022.

Watson, M. L. 1958. Staining of tissue sections for electron microscopy and heavy metals. II. Application of solutions containing lead and barium. *J. Biophys. Biochem. Cytol.*, 4: 727–730.

Watson, M. L., and Avery, J. K. 1954. The development of the hamster lower incisor as observed by electron microscopy. *Am. J. Anat.*, 95: 109–137.

11

Chemistry of the Protein Matrix of Enamel

KARL A. PIEZ
National Institute of Dental Research, National Institutes of Health, Bethesda,
Maryland

The justification for including this subject in a symposium on keratinization arises from the fact that the protein of enamel is of epithelial origin and has some of the morphological properties of the keratins. Although enamel protein has for this reason generally been called a keratin, the classification has never been entirely satisfactory. For example, unlike the typical keratins, enamel protein occurs normally in a highly calcified state. With the rapid advances in recent years in techniques for studying proteins, it is now possible to clarify the question of the nature of this rather strange protein. The large amount of work necessary to do this has only just begun, but it is already clear that enamel protein in not a keratin in the sense that hair and epidermal proteins are keratins. Rather, it is a unique material which has some of the properties of both the keratins and the collagens. It is proposed here to document and expand on this general conclusion primarily from the standpoint of the chemistry of the protein but also to discuss other pertinent data obtained by x-ray diffraction and observations on solubility.

Enamel is a highly calcified tissue containing, in the mature human tooth, about 0.4% protein. Probably the greatest problem in studying the matrix arises in obtaining a sufficient quantity of a pure sample. The enamel lies in close proximity to dentin and is difficult to separate cleanly from it. This source of contamination is compounded by the fact that dentin contains about forty times as much protein, mostly in the form of a typical collagen, as enamel. Therefore, a 1% contamination before decalcification becomes about 30% after the protein is decalcified. If it also happens that the enamel protein is lost more easily than the impurities during preparation, the sample may, in the end, consist mostly of contaminants. It is likely that impurities arising in this manner have affected many of the results of chemical studies of enamel matrix which have so far been reported. The early data in the literature (Hess and Lee, 1954; Stack, 1954; Battistone and Burnett, 1956), although contradictory in some respects, are so close to the values that would be obtained for a collagen that it is necessary to conclude either that enamel protein is a collagen or that the samples were grossly impure. Undoubtedly the latter is the case since very different results have recently been obtained in three different laboratories. We have studied human adult and pig embryo enamel; Eastoe (1960) has analyzed human fetal enamel; Glimcher and Mechanic (1961) have examined calf enamel. Brief discussions of some of our results have appeared (Piez, 1960, 1961; Piez and Likins, 1960).

Our human enamel samples were prepared as follows. Teeth were cleaned by grinding off a thin layer of enamel over the whole crown. The crown was then cut into small pieces, sacrificing areas containing pits and fissures and any discolored enamel, and the dentin was removed by grinding with frequent examination under a dissecting microscope. Considerable enamel was sacrificed to minimize the possibility of leaving any dentin. All grinding was done with appropriate dental tools under a stream of water. Three types of samples were prepared in this way: (1) enamel from unerupted third molars recently extracted and preserved by freezing; (2) enamel from unerupted third molars preserved by storage in formaldehyde, often for several years or more; (3) enamel from random extracted teeth, both carious and sound. A fourth sample consisted of pig embryo enamel supplied by Drs. Lefkowitz and Forscher of the University of Kansas City Dental School. This was prepared by microdissection of partially calcified teeth. All possible care was taken to exclude cells and membranes on the forming surface of the enamel and dentin from the inner surface. As will be seen, all these samples contained at least small amounts of dentin in spite of the careful isolation procedures.

The samples were powdered, suspended in water, and placed in cellophane bags. The bags were placed in beakers containing 10% ethylene diaminetetracetic acid (pH 7.5, at 5°C) which was stirred gently. Decalcification was allowed to proceed until complete, 7 to 10 days, and the chelating agent was removed by exhaustive dialysis against water. The residues were isolated by centrifugation and the supernatants were lyophilized. This procedure gives a soluble and an insoluble macromolecular fraction; low molecular weight material is lost.

The enamel sample from random extracted teeth yielded essentially no protein either soluble or insoluble. The trace of insoluble residue, amounting to no more than a few milligrams from about 6 grams of enamel, could be seen under the microscope to be mostly debris and small bits of decalcified dentin which escaped the careful dissection. Its analysis also indicated it to be largely dentin collagen. This type of sample is probably similar to those analyzed by others (Hess and Lee, 1954; Stack, 1954; Battistone and Burnett, 1956) as enamel matrix. The unerupted third molars, preserved by freezing, also did not yield satisfactory amounts of matrix. No soluble fraction and only a very small insoluble fraction was obtained which, on the basis of its hydroxyproline content, was about half collagen. By far the best sources were the formaldehyde-preserved human unerupted third molars and the pig embryo teeth. Because of rather large mechanical losses due to the small amounts of material which it was necessary to handle, it was not possible to calculate exact yields. From the formaldehyde-preserved teeth, approximately 0.2% of the calcified enamel was obtained in the form of organic material which was approximately equally divided between the soluble and insoluble fractions. Yields several times this were obtained from the pig embryo teeth since they were only partially calcified. In this case also about half of the protein was soluble after decalcification and dialysis.

The various samples were hydrolyzed in a large excess of 6N hydrochloric acid in a sealed tube with a nitrogen atmosphere for

24 hours at 106°C. The acid was removed by concentration *in vacuo,* and portions equivalent to 1 to 2 mg of protein were analyzed for their amino acid content by employing an automatic instrument (Piez and Morris, 1960). Tryptophan, which is destroyed

Table I.   Amino Acid Composition of Enamel Proteins
(Residues/1000 total residues)

| | Human Dentin Collagen | Pig Embryo Enamel | | | Human Enamel,[b] Soluble | Human Fetal Enamel [c] |
| | | Soluble | Insoluble | | | |
			Found	Corrected [a]		
Cysteic acid	0	0	0	0	12 [d]	—
Hydroxyproline	99	0	16	0	0	0
Aspartic acid	46	29	50	51	83	30
Threonine	17	37	41	45	58	38
Serine	33	46	71	78	76	63
Glutamic acid	74	185	113	121	144	142
Proline	116	271	147	152	146	251
Glycine	329	49	123	84	97	65
Alanine	112	24	30	14	56	20
Cystine	0	0	0	0	0	4
Valine	25	37	32	33	45	40
Methionine	5.3	47	40	47	21	42
Isoleucine	9.3	32	28	31	30	33
Leucine	24	94	79	90	96	91
Tyrosine	6.4	22	49	57	0 [e]	53
Phenylalanine	16	26	37	41	51	23
Hydroxylysine	9.6	1.6	2.1	0.8	3.4	0
Lysine	22	11	25	25	21	18
Histidine	4.7	72	50	58	30	65
Arginine	52	6.1	34	31	31	23
Tryptophan[f]	0	12	35	42	—	—

[a] Corrected on the assumption that the hydroxyproline found represents contamination with dentin collagen having a composition the same as human dentin collagen.

[b] From unerupted third molars preserved in formaldehyde.

[c] Eastoe (1960).

[d] This is a tentative identification. If correct, the cysteic acid presumably arose by oxidation of cystine. It is also possible that the material is an artifact produced by the action of the formaldehyde preservative.

[e] Tyrosine may have been destroyed during the period of preservation.

[f] Determined from the ultraviolet spectra (Beaven and Holiday, 1952).

by acid hydrolysis, was determined by ultraviolet spectroscopy (Beaven and Holiday, 1952) when sufficient sample was available.

The results are assembled in Table I. The data are expressed as residues of each amino acid per thousand total residues to allow a ready comparison on an equivalent basis. The insoluble proteins from the enamel of unerupted human third molars whether preserved by freezing or in formaldehyde were very similar after correction for the presence of dentin collagen (see below). This was also true of the soluble and insoluble fractions from the formaldehyde-preserved human teeth. Therefore only the analysis of the soluble fraction of the formaldehyde-preserved human teeth is presented in the table. The analyses of both fractions from the pig embryo teeth are included, together with the results after correction, to illustrate the type of data obtained. For purposes of comparison, an analysis of human dentin collagen and the results reported by Eastoe (1960) for human fetal enamel matrix are presented. A typical chromatogram showing the analysis of the soluble protein fraction of pig embryo enamel matrix appears in Fig. 1.

All the samples that were insoluble after decalcification contained hydroxyproline, an imino acid generally indicative of collagen. If the assumption is made that the hydroxyproline arose from the incomplete removal of dentin collagen, the analytical values can be corrected on the basis of the composition of dentin collagen. Only human dentin has been analyzed, but this should be satisfactory for both the pig and human samples since all vertebrate collagens are very similar (Piez and Likins, 1960). However, the validity of the assumption that all the hydroxyproline represents contamination bears careful examination. Since the soluble fractions reported here contained no hydroxyproline and Eastoe (1960) found none in his matrix sample, this would seem to be the most obvious explanation. The finding of variable amounts of hydroxyproline in other samples is also consistent with the presence of impurities. Undoubtedly it can be concluded that the major portion of the hydroxyproline in our insoluble fractions and in the samples studied by early investigators (Hess and Lee, 1954; Stack, 1954; Battistone and Burnett, 1956) was from dentin collagen, but the presence of a small amount of hydroxyproline as a natural constituent of enamel

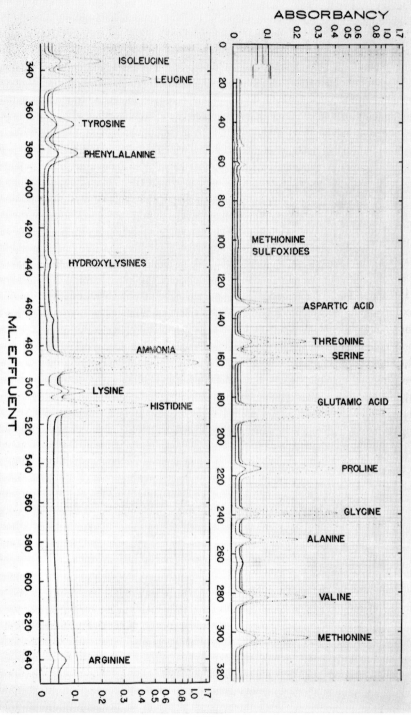

matrix cannot be completely ruled out. First of all, small amounts of hydroxyproline, less than about 2 residues per 1000, in the soluble fractions would not have been seen by us owing to the poor color yield of this imino acid. Also Burroughs (1961) has reported finding trace amounts of hydroxyproline in human enamel matrix by using sensitive analytical methods and highly refined isolation technics to ensure the absence of dentin. However, unequivocable proof will come only when the protein of enamel can be purified and characterized particularly with regard to homogeneity. Until this is done it can always be argued that contaminants are present.

An important finding is the presence of hydroxylysine, another amino acid characteristic of collagen, in the matrix samples. The amount in the insoluble fraction of pig embryo enamel cannot be determined accurately because the hydroxylysine content of collagen is variable, and it is not certain that the amount in human dentin collagen, used for the correction, is the same as in pig dentin collagen. However, the 2 to 3 residues per 1000 total residues present in the soluble fractions of both pig embryo and human enamel matrices are significant. This amount could not have come from collagen since 20 to 30% contamination would be necessary which would have been readily detected by the presence of hydroxyproline, as in the case of the insoluble fractions. The identification of this amino acid as hydroxylysine can be considered to be certain. It not only moves to a characteristic position on the chromatogram but more important it forms a double peak of a characteristic shape owing to the presence of two optical isomers (diastereoisomers) that move at slightly different rates on the ion

---

Fig. 1. A strip-chart chromatogram showing an amino acid analysis of the soluble fraction of the protein matrix from pig embryo enamel. The amino acids were separated by ion exchange chromatography and detected by the ninhydrin reaction. An automatic instrument (Piez and Morris, 1960) was employed which monitors the color at 440 mμ (upper trace in baseline regions of the chromatogram) and at 570 mμ in two cells of different light paths (middle and lower trace in baseline regions). The gradually increasing baseline results from the changing composition of the buffer used to elute the amino acids. The color yields of the amino acids are approximately equal except for proline (absorbing maximally at 440 mμ) which gives about one fourth the color of other amino acids (absorbing maximally at 570 mμ). The peak following alanine is tentatively identified as galactosamine.

exchange column (Piez, 1954; Piez and Morris, 1960). The relative amounts of the two isomers are also in agreement with predicted behavior (Piez, 1954). Although these peaks are small, they can be seen in Fig. 1 at about 440 ml of effluent. This pattern is reproducible and unique.

The function of hydroxylysine is not known, although there is suggestive evidence that it may have some special role (Piez, 1961). Until recently it had been identified only in collagen. A recent report indicates that it is also present in trypsin and chrymotrypsin (Viswanatha and Irreverre, 1960). The amounts found in calcified mammalian collagens vary between species and tissues within the same animal from about 4 to 16 residues per 1000 residues with a compensating increase or decrease in the lysine content. Although no correlation between hydroxylysine/lysine ratio and tissue has been found, no other amino acid pair varies in this manner (Piez and Likins, 1960).

Another distinctive feature of the amino acid compositions of these enamel samples is the presence of large amounts of proline. In the case of the soluble fraction of pig embryo matrix more than one-quarter of the total residues are proline. Eastoe (1960) found nearly as much in human fetal enamel protein. The other samples contain less but still more than most other proteins including mammalian collagens (Piez and Likins, 1960). The importance of this observation lies in the fact that proline, like hydroxyproline but unlike all other commonly occurring amino acids, is a cyclic imino acid containing a pyrrolidine ring. The ring structure prevents free rotation about the bond between the α-carbon and the nitrogen. This places certain restrictions on the configuration which a polypeptide chain can assume in the vicinity of a proline residue. For example, the α-helix which is common to α-keratins and many globular proteins cannot be formed if proline is present. Although a detailed discussion is not possible here, it would be expected that the most stable structure for a protein containing as much proline as found in enamel matrix would be a polyproline-type helix, at least over some parts of the polypeptide chain. Since a similar type of configuration is found in all collagens, it may be that enamel matrix and collagen have some structural features in common, although direct evidence is lacking. These very important considerations have been reviewed by Harrington and von Hipple (1961) with regard to the structure of collagen and gelatin.

The amino acid analyses of the enamel matrices presented in Table I have some additional points of interest. Histidine is present in very much larger amounts than in most other proteins. This is particularly apparent when the amount is compared to the content of other basic amino acids which are usually present at much higher levels than histidine. Glutamic acid is a major amino acid in these proteins not often found in these amounts. The glycine values are typical of other proteins and are very much lower than occur in collagen. Collagens consistently contain glycine to the extent of approximately one-third of their total residues (Gross and Piez, 1960; Piez and Likins, 1960). This is a necessary requirement for the triple-chain structure of this group of proteins (Rich and Crick, 1958) and definitely precludes on a chemical basis the classification of enamel protein as a collagen. Cystine is absent from these samples. Since this is often cited as an important chemical criterion for a keratin, it would appear, also on a chemical basis, that enamel protein does not fit in this group either.

It should be possible to answer some of the structural questions raised by the chemical results by x-ray diffraction methods. Pautard (1961) and Glimcher et al. (1961) have obtained diffraction patterns with partial orientation which are typical of the group of proteins classified crystallographically as cross β-keratins. It is generally believed that this group of proteins differs from the normal β-keratins in that the polypeptide chains are folded back and forth on themselves rather than being extended, but that the chains otherwise have the same structure (Crick and Kendrew, 1957). The pattern is most often seen as an artifact resulting from chemical and physical changes in a β-keratin of the normal type. This raises the question whether the present observations may also result from artifacts. It is also important to remember that only a small part of a sample need have order to give a distinctive pattern. The x-ray diffraction patterns themselves indicate the presence of a large amount, perhaps well over half, of disordered material. This means that no structure can at present be assigned to all the enamel protein. Definitive x-ray data can be obtained only if better samples can be prepared.

The observations on enamel yields and solubilities may be pertinent to the problem of enamel maturation. Enamel of adult human teeth yielded no appreciable amount of protein after decalcification and even unerupted third molars preserved by freezing gave only a very small amount of matrix heavily contaminated with collagen while third molars preserved in formaldehyde, but otherwise identical, provided both soluble and insoluble protein. The obvious conclusion is that the matrix in adult unfixed teeth is largely dialyzable since it could have gone nowhere else. Formaldehyde, by virtue of its crosslinking action, presumably produced protein molecules sufficiently large to be either insoluble or retained in solution in the dialysis sacks. The observation that both soluble and insoluble protein could also be isolated from pig embryo teeth indicates that the matrix is originally laid down in a highly polymerized form and therefore that some type of change occurs as the teeth age to produce lower molecular weight material. Eastoe (1960) hydrolyzed and analyzed his enamel sample without decalcification and so presents no data on solubility.

In considering the various suggestions put forth above it must be remembered that no information is as yet available on the homogeneity of enamel protein. Certainly the fractions so far analyzed are heterogeneous as indicated by the solubilities, but it is not clear whether this applies to the native protein as it is secreted by the cell, whether it is a natural development as a function of time, or whether it occurs during the preparation of the sample. Therefore the matrix may well contain several proteins having quite different properties. This could explain some of the apparent anomalies.

In summary, it is apparent that enamel protein is not a keratin in the same sense as the other proteins discussed in this symposium. However, it is like the keratins in that it is of epithelial origin, and it appears to have some structural features of the β-keratins, as determined by x-ray diffraction. The protein is also related to the collagens in that it contains hydroxylysine, perhaps hydroxyproline, and large amounts of proline.

REFERENCES

Battistone, G. C., and Burnett, G. W. 1956. Studies on the composition of teeth. IV. The amino acid composition of human enamel protein. *J. Dental Research*, 35: 260.

Beaven, G. H., and Holiday, E. R. 1952. Ultraviolet absorption spectra of proteins and amino acids. *Advances in Protein Chem.*, 7: 320.

Burroughs, L. R. 1961. Hydroxyproline in enamel. *J. Dental Research, 40*: 749.

Crick, F. H. C., and Kendrew, J. C. 1957. X-ray analysis and protein structure. *Advances in Protein Chem., 12*: 134.

Eastoe, J. E. 1960. Organic matrix of tooth enamel. *Nature, 187*: 411.

Glimcher, M. J., Bonar, L. C., and Daniel, E. J. 1961. The molecular structure of the protein matrix of bovine dental enamel. *J. Molecular Biol., 3*: 541.

Glimcher, M. J., and Mechanic, J. 1961. *J. Biol. Chem., 236*: 3210.

Gross, J., and Piez, K. A. 1960. The nature of collagen. I. Invertebrate collagens. *Calcification in Biological Systems*, Reidar F. Sognnaes, Editor. American Association for the Advancement of Science, Washington, D.C. P. 395.

Harrington, W. F., and von Hippel, P. H. 1961. The structure of collagen and gelatin. *Advances in Protein Chem., 16*: 1.

Hess, W. C., and Lee, C. 1954. The amino acid composition of proteins isolated from the healthy enamel and dentin of carious teeth. *J. Dental Research, 31*: 791.

Pautard, F. G. E. 1961. An x-ray diffraction pattern from human enamel matrix. *Arch. Oral Bio., 3*: 217.

Piez, K. A. 1954. The separation of the diastereoisomers of isoleucine and hydroxylysine by ion exchange chromatography. *J. Biol. Chem., 207*: 77.

Piez, K. A. 1960. The nature of the protein matrix of human enamel. *J. Dental Research, 39*: 712.

Piez, K. A. 1961. The amino acid composition of the proteins from some calcified tissues. *Science, 134*: 841.

Piez, K. A., and Likins, R. C. 1960. The nature of collagen. II. Vertebrate collagens. *Calcification in Biological Systems*, Reidar F. Sognnaes, Editor. American Association for the Advancement of Science, Washington, D.C. P. 411.

Piez, K. A., and Morris, L. 1960. A modified procedure for the automatic analysis of amino acids. *Anal. Biochem., 1*: 187.

Rich, A., and Crick, F. H. C. 1958. The structure of collagen. *Recent*

Advances in Gelatin and Glue Research, Pergamon Press, New York. P. 20.

Stack, M. V. 1954. Organic constituents of enamel. *J. Am. Dental Assoc.,* 48: 297.

Viswanatha, T., and Irreverre, F. 1960. The occurrence of hydroxylysine in trypsin. *Biochim. et Biophys. Acta, 40*: 564.

Index

Acanthosis, 113
Adult
  epidermis, basal cell differentiation, 55
  skin cultures, 53, 59
  skin samples, human, 11
Ameloblasts, 165, 168
Amphibia
  keratins, 29
Arginine, 27

Beak, 5
  of ducks, 36
Birds
  keratins, 29
  spurs, 35
Bizzozero
  nodes of, 143

Calluses, 2
Cells
  appearance of keratinized, 63
  behavior, 47
  cultures, vitamin A, 101
  germinative, 4, 5
  transformation, 13
Cement
  amorphous, 2, 8
  amorphous interfibrillary, 9
  filament-cement ratio, 8
Claws, 2, 5, 29
  hard keratin, 28, 77
  sulfhydryl-positive, 35
Colchicine
  mitotic studies, 100

Collagen, 175
  enamel, 182
  hydroxylysine, 179
Cornea
  epithelium, 121
  vitamin A effect on, 119, 121, 123, 128
Corns, 2
Cortex
  of hair, 29
Cysteine, 2
Cystine
  enamel proteins, 181
Cysts, see also *Keratocysts*
  dental, 151, 158
  follicular, 151
  nonkeratinized, 157
  odontogenic, 152, 153, 159
  primordial, 151
  residual, 152
Cytomorphic changes, 4
Cytoplasmic constituents, 2
Cytoplasmic fibrils, 6, 22
  occurrence, 10
  properties, 19
Cytoplasmic filaments, 16
Cytoplasmic granules
  amorphous, 3, 6, 22
Cytoplasmic organelles, 79, 106

Dental cysts, 158
  epithelium, 151
Dentin, 165, 175
Dentino-enamel junction, 167
Desmosomes, 13, 65, 69, 165

Detergents
  stratum corneum, 136
Disulfides, 2, 28, 40
  distribution, 37
  epidermis, 37
  feathers, 36
  in hair, 31, 33
  in lamprey teeth, 35
  in nails, 35
  vertebrate keratins, 39
Dopa oxidase, 10
Ducks, 36
Dyskeratosis, 55

Earle's solution, 21
Electron microscope
  investigations, keratinization, 6,
    11, 61
  keratohyalin granules, 21
Embryonic skin cultures, 55, 59
Enamel
  cultures, 51, 59
  extracellular, 169, 170
  human, 174
  hydroxyproline, 177
  insoluble proteins, 177
  matrix, 39
  maturation, 182
  protein, 173, 182
  sheath, 167
Endoplasmic reticulum
  cells of tongue, 168
Epidermis, 2, 55
  disulfides in, 37
  human, 16
  sheets, *in vitro*, 49
  sulfhydryls in, 37
  thickening, 100
  ultraviolet irradiation, 137
  vitamin A growth effect, 53
Epithelium
  of cheek, 143
  of dental cysts, 151
  ectodermal, 59

Epithelium (*Continued*)
  palatal, 143
  vaginal, 39, 96
  vitamin A effect on, 106, 121
Eponychium, 2
Esophagus, 62
Estrogen
  nipple response, 101
Explants
  adult skin, 55
Eye washings
  vitamin A, 12

Feathers, 5, 40
  disulfides, 36
Feulgen-negative, 10
Filaments, 8
Fish, 29
Fluids
  loss of, 18
Follicles
  cysts, 151

Gingiva
  human, 142
  parakeratosis, 139
Glands
  sebaceous, 58, 127
  sweat, 57, 134
Glutamic acid
  enamel matrix, 181
Glycogen, 139
Golgi material, 65, 89
Granules
  size, 6
Guinea pig, 8
  vitamin A, 100

Hair, 2
  cortical cell line, 2, 4, 6
  growth *in vitro*, 58
  medullary cells, 4
  root sheaths, 6, 37
  vitamin A, 127

Hair cuticle
  amorphous, 79
  cell line, 3, 6
Hair feathers, 36
Hair follicles, 2
  root sheath, 8
  soft keratin, 70
  in vitro, 53
Hamster
  cheek pouch, mucous metaplasia,
    101
  cheek pouch, vitamin A, 101
Hard keratin, 2, 4, 28, 41, 85; see
    also *Keratins; Soft keratin*
  difference from soft keratin, 77
  formation, 89
  hair and claw, 77
  structure, 83
Hematoxylin-Biebrich Scarlet, 18
Henle's layer, 73
Histidine, 27
  enamel matrix, 181
Hoofs, 2, 5
  hard keratin, 28
  rhinoceros, 29
Hormones, 4
Horns, 2, 5, 40
  hard keratin, 28
Horny material, 4, 6, 18
  amorphous, 8
  cells, 4, 5
  fibrous, 4, 7–9
  horse, 29
Horse
  burr, 2
  hoofs, 29
Humidity
  stratum corneum, 133
Huxley's layer, 74
Hydrophilic components
  stratum corneum, 135
Hydroxylysine, 179, 180
Hydroxyproline, 175, 177
Hyperkeratosis, 96

Hypertrophy
  epidermal, 100

Inflammation, 139
Irradiation, 137

α-Keratin, 2, 180
β-Keratin, 181
Keratins, see also *Hard keratin; Soft
    keratin*
  amorphous, 6, 62, 89
  chemical features, 27
  precursors, 4
  types, 27
Keratocysts, 152; see also *Cysts*
  diastase-resistant cells, 158
  Mallory-stained sections, 155
Keratohyalin granules, 8, 10, 49, 89,
    90
  content, 40
  disintegration, 16
  in epidermis, 11
  isolation technic, 21, 22
  location, 13, 65
  origin, 67
  properties, 18, 19, 22
  RNA relation, 91
  RNP relation, 67
  shape, 13
  transformation, 16, 85

Lamprey teeth, 33
Lysine, 27
Melanocytes, 49, 53
Metaplasia
  alteration, 95
  hamster cheek pouch, 101, 106
  mucous, 104, 106
  squamous, 119
  vitamin A, 58, 104
Methacrylate
  embedding medium, 63
Micro-environment
  relative humidity, 135

Microvilli, 65
Mitochondria, 13, 79
  ameloblasts, 165
  distribution, 65
Mitosis
  vitamin A effect on, 121
Mitotic index, 97, 121, 125
  epidermis, 100
Morphology, 6
Mouse
  cheek mitotic rates, 147
  skin, 97
Mouth
  keratin layer, 143
Mucopolysaccharides, 10
Mucosa
  alveolar, unkeratinized, 141
Mucous membranes, 95

Nails, 2, 5, 29, 40
  hard keratin, 28

Oleic acid, 99
Organ cultures
  glands, 51
  molar teeth, 51
Organelles
  cytoplasmic, 79, 106
Orthokeratinization, 147
  occurrence, 142
Osmiophilic bodies, 104
Osmium tetroxide, 11, 62

Parakeratosis, 55, 103
  membranes, 40
  oral mucous membrane, 141
Polypeptide chains, 2
Porcupine quills, 29, 37
Prekeratin, 5, 28
Proline, 180
Proteins
  amorphous, 8

Quills, 5, 6
  porcupine, 29, 37

Rat, see also *Rodent*
  epidermis of newborn, 11
  vaginal epithelium, 96
  vitamin A effect on skin, 97
Reptiles, 29
Rhinoceros
  hoofs, 29
  horn, 37
Ribonuclease, 10
Ribonucleic acid (RNA), 10
Ribonucleoprotein (RNP), 65, 90
  particles, 67, 69, 74, 79, 81, 89, 168
RNA, see *Ribonucleic acid*
RNP, see *Ribonucleoprotein*
Rodent, see also *Rat*
  claw, 35
  oral cavity, 146

Scales
  snake, 36
S^{35}-cysteine
  vitamin A effect, 106
Sebaceous glands, 58
  vitamin A, 127
Sebum
  cementing effect, 136
Skin
  adult, 49
  embryonic, 49, 59
  explants, 47
  samples of human adult, 11
  vitamin A, 100
S^{35}-labeled sulfate
  enamel, 168
Snake
  scales, 36
Soft keratin, 2, 4, 28, 37, 40, 62; see
    also *Hard keratin; Keratins*
  esophagus, 63
  formation, 88
  skin, 63
  structure, 81
  tongue, 63

Spurs
  of birds, 35
—S—S— bonds, 19, 22
  site of, 9
Starvation cultures, 57
Stratum corneum, 136
  physical characteristics, 137
  water supply, 134–136
Sulfhydryls, 29, 35, 36, 40
  enamel matrix, 39
  free, 28, 36
  groups, 2, 22
  hair, 29, 33
  tooth bud, 33
Sulfur, 2, 4, 8, 9, 28
Sweat glands, 57, 134

Teeth
  of lamprey, 29
Tissue
  connective, 57
  vitamin A-deficient, 113
Tonofibrils, 2, 4, 6, 143
  clumped, 16
  epithelium of cheek, 143
Tonofilaments, 69, 79
  size, 67
  soft keratin, 81
Tongue, 62
Trachea
  vitamin A, 126
Trichohyalin granules, 8, 73, 74, 77
  reaction, 37
Trypsin, 47
  effects on epidermis, 11
  resistance of keratohyalin granules, 18

Ultraviolet irradiation
  epidermis, 137
Uranyl nitrate, 8

Vaginal epithelium, 39
  estrogen effect, 96
  vitamin A effect, 97
Vitamin A, 59, 95, 108
  antikeratinization effect, 115
  cell division, 100
  chick skin, 101
  deficiency, 95, 113, 118
  dose, 108, 128
  effect on cornea, 119, 121, 123, 128
  effect on epidermal hypertrophy, 100
  effect on mitosis, 121
  effects on epithelia, 106, 121
  enamel organs, 58
  excess, 95, 96
  growth effect on epidermis, 53
  guinea pig nipple, 100
  hair, 99
  hamster cheek pouch, 104
  leukoplakia, 107
  metaplastic effect, 58
  mouse skin, 97
  mucous metaplasia, 104
  skin of man, 100
  skin of rat, 97
  S^{35}-sulfate, 106
  supply and use, 47
  utilization, 128
  vaginal epithelium, 97
Vitamins, 4

Wool, 5, 6
  proteins of, 9